7

CLIENT-LED DESIGN

The McGraw-Hill Information Systems, Management and Strategy Series

Series Coordinator
Dr Nimal Jayaratna
Heriot-Watt University
Edinburgh

Series Board

Professor Trevor Wood-Harper	Salford University
Professor Bob Galliers	Warwick Business School
Dr Steve Smithson	London School of Economics
Mr Bob Wood	Salford University
Dr Patrik Holt	Heriot-Watt University
Dr Frank Stowell	University of Paisley
Dr Daune West	University of Paisley
Dr Ray Miles	North East Wales Institute
Professor Hans-Erik Nissen	Lund University
Professor Jean-Michael Larrasquet	Université de Pau et des Pays L'Adour
Professor Tom Wilson	University of Sheffield

Further Titles in this Series

Understanding and Evaluating Methodologies:
Nimsad—a systemic Framework
Nimal Jayaratna

Information Management
Andrew Mortimer

Information Systems Provision
Edited by Frank Stowell

CLIENT-LED DESIGN
A Systemic Approach to Information System Definition

Frank Stowell

Professor of Information Systems
Department of Computing and
Information Systems
University of Paisley

Daune West

Senior Lecturer
Department of Computing and
Information Systems
University of Paisley

McGRAW-HILL BOOK COMPANY

London • New York • St Louis • San Francisco • Auckland • Bogotá
Caracas • Lisbon • Madrid • Mexico • Milan •Montreal
New Delhi • Panama • Paris • San Juan • São Paulo
Singapore • Sydney • Tokyo • Toronto

Published by
McGRAW-HILL Book Company Europe
Shoppenhangers Road, Maidenhead, Berkshire, SL6 2QL, England
Telephone 0628 23432
Fax 0628 770224

British Library Cataloguing in Publication Data

The CIP data for this title is available from the British Library, UK.

Library of Congress Cataloging-in-Publication Data

The CIP data for this title is available from the Library of Congress,
Washington DC, USA.

12345 CUP 97654

ISBN 0-07-707824-1

Typeset by Datix International Limited,
Bungay, Suffolk
and printed and bound in Great Britain at the University Press, Cambridge

CONTENTS

PREFACE   vii

ACKNOWLEDGEMENTS   xi

PART I   THE FOUNDATIONS OF CLIENT-LED DESIGN   1

1   INFORMATION SYSTEMS AND COMPUTING   3
     Introduction   3
     Computer systems   3
     Market pressures   6
     Thinking about information systems   11
     Information systems: a definition   21
     The need for client-led design   22
     Review questions   23
     Exercises   24

2   SYSTEMS THINKING AS A BASIS FOR CLIENT-LED DESIGN   25
     Introduction   25
     Contextual issues: organizational culture   25
     The management of change   28
     A method to support client-led design   31
     Implications of client-led design   37
     The contribution of systems thinking to client-led design   40
     Systems concepts   42
     System description   47
     Review questions   52
     Exercises   52

3   DESCRIBING AND MODELLING SYSTEMS USING SYSTEMS TOOLS   54
     Introduction: the 'appreciative' setting   54
     Models and modelling   55
     Defining a notional system   57
     Systems diagrams and models for Phase I   60
     Summary   89
     Review questions   89
     Exercises   89

4   A VIEW OF ORGANIZATIONS FOR CLIENT-LED DESIGN
     OF INFORMATION SYSTEMS   91
     Introduction   91
     What is a business organization?   92
     Goal-seeking models of organization   95
     Equilibrium models of organization   103
     Relationship-maintaining models of organization   108
     Interpretive systems thinking   109
     Interpretive organizational analysis   114
     Vickers' appreciative system as a basis for CLD   118

Review questions 119
Exercises 120

5 ACTION RESEARCH: A METHOD FOR CLIENT-LED DESIGN 121
Introduction 121
The positivist empiricist perspective 121
Value-neutrality of methods 123
Action research as a framework for social enquiry 126
Summary 135

PART II THE PRACTICE OF CLIENT-LED DESIGN **137**

6 CLIENT-LED DESIGN: THE WAVERLY–RANDALL CASE STUDY 138
Introduction 138
Phase I (Appreciation): the problem situation 140
Members of staff at Waverly–Randall 144
Waverly–Randall: overview of the company 154
The project 159
Review 170
Exercises 170

7 CLIENT-LED DESIGN: INFORMATION SYSTEM DESCRIPTION
AND TECHNICAL SPECIFICATION 172
Introduction 172
Translation and validation 173
Creating job descriptions 177
Technical specification 179
Training and implementation 196
Summary 199
Exercises 199

8 THE BLACKWOOD CITY LIBRARY CASE STUDY 201
Introduction 201
The case study scenario 202
Case study material 202
The city of Blackwood 215
Blackwood City Library 218
Case study project 225
Task outline 225

END NOTE 233
The case studies 234
Information systems analyst 234
Conclusion 235

REFERENCES 236

INDEX 247

PREFACE

THE CHANGING ROLE OF THE COMPUTER SYSTEMS ANALYST

The developments in information technology (IT) in the latter part of the 1980s and the early 1990s has been matched by the growth in the number and roles of the various IT specialists (e.g. software engineers, AI specialists, knowledge engineers). In particular, the responsibilities and tasks of the computer systems analyst (CSA) have changed significantly during this period, suggesting that a review of the role and the title of the CSA is long overdue.

The title 'computer systems analyst', often (and incorrectly) referred to as 'systems analyst', has connotations of number-crunching mainframe computers, data-driven design methods and data-processing systems. However, the expectations of clients, influenced by the availability, flexibility and variety of current information technology, have played an important role in the reassessment of the role of the CSA. The result is that the title of 'systems analyst' is inappropriate to the type of role and activities that are now being undertaken by, or expected of, the modern information systems professional. As a reflection of this changing role more common titles in use today include: information systems analyst, information systems designer, and information systems architect. In this text we shall refer to the professional as an information system analyst (ISA) as we believe that this title reflects the change in emphasis from computing to information systems while maintaining reference to the important underlying notion of 'analysis' that has been carried over from the days of true 'systems analysis' (i.e. RAND Corporation's systems analysis). The breadth of expertise that this new role demands means that in addition to a change in title the modern ISA should develop and possess a wide range of skills, which include not only technical expertise but also knowledge that is commonly associated with the social sciences.

Since the 1970s, CSAs began to recognize that the introduction of computer systems produced significant changes to organizational behaviour and often resulted in staff resistance to the implementation of the computer system. Recognizing such reactions, practitioners and researchers began to re-evaluate the methods by which computer systems were designed and developed (Methlie, 1980; Miles,1985; Stowell, 1985; Avison and Wood-Harper, 1986; Buckingham et al. 1987; Lyytinen and Klein, 1985; Hirschheim and Newman, 1988; Bell and Wood-Harper, 1992). Practitioners saw that many of the methods of computer systems analysis currently in use were inadequate in coping with the social and technical dimensions of the problem situation. In investigating the history and development of these methods it was highlighted that it was not unusual for computer systems analysis methods to be developed in an *ad hoc* fashion, often to meet a particular set of needs. These methods were then re-used in other projects and, in time, became established computer systems analysis methodology. The process of introducing computer-based data-processing systems into an enterprise was recognized by researchers as creating difficulties in the wider context of organizational activities (Mumford and Henshall, 1979; Klein and Hirschheim, 1983; Land, 1985; Kling, 1987).

A further dimension to the latter problem has been the development of relatively cheap, large capacity and fast response personal computers, which has meant that the user or client has become more 'computer literate'. Home computers, computers at school and the commonality of desktop machines in the work environment means that relatively few people are unaware of the potential of computing power. The way in which computers are used in a business has become the concern of all those who work in the enterprise rather than solely that of a limited number of technical 'specialists'. Together, these problem areas have caused many information systems professionals to re-evaluate the way in which they undertake their duties, which has resulted in 'new' approaches to information systems development aimed at enabling the clients' views to become more fully represented than in the past (Mumford and Henshall, 1979; Wilson, 1984, and 1990; Wood-Harper and Fitzgerald, 1982; Wood-Harper *et al.* 1985; Arison and Wood-Harper, 1990; Stowell, 1985, 1991; Stowell and West, 1994; Miles, 1985; Finklestein, 1989).

It would be a mistake to assume that the blame for client dissatisfaction was solely that of the ISA. Many ISAs take care to embrace client requirements within their design process but their clients do not always appreciate the problem situation as a whole, nor are they able to perceive the full ramifications of the potential IT-based information system upon the working practices of the enterprise.

The ISA has to deal with the difficulties of problem appreciation, problem definition and analysis, the technical design, implementation and maintenance. We can represent this set of activities as five phases of an information system development, the operation of which we shall refer to within the method of client-led design (CLD):

- *PHASE I*   Problem 'appreciation', definition and analysis
- *PHASE II* Definition of the information system
- *PHASE III* Definition of supporting technology
- *PHASE IV* Implementation of the technology-supported information system
- *PHASE V*   Maintenance, development and review of the technology supported information system, review of the problem situation (Phase I)

Many of the approaches to computer system development are ideally suited to the technical specification stage of the development cycle (Phase III onwards) but these approaches have often squeezed out the important and foundational activities which we identify under Phase I and much of Phase II. The result of missing out Phase I, in particular, can be a technically sound design which does not satisfy the client because its implementation is met with resistance and, subsequently, it fails to fulfil its potential (e.g. Rzevski, 1988; Stowell and West, 1992). Even technical specifications which appear to meet the clients' original requirements sometimes fail since the clients may review and adjust their requirements throughout the project as they learn more about (a) their working practices and procedures and (b) the potential benefits of applying technology to their work. There is evidence to suggest that many IT projects are not evaluated after implementation with little or no lessons learned from experience (Willcocks and Lester, 1993). A serious difficulty for the information systems profes- sional is that of appreciating the business and the managerial problems in their widest context. Often the technology-driven design methods that are used deny the practi- tioner the opportunity to take into account potential changes to business practices and procedures because of the concentration upon improving (usually in the form of speeding-up) current methods of operating. Added to which, the preoccupation of many practitioners with computers often prevents the consideration of other technologies that could form part of a well-defined information system.

One further difficulty for the modern information systems professional concerns the notion of an information system itself. Many of the ideas that supported computer systems development since the 1970s are no longer relevant to the current ideas about information systems: a new era of thinking has evolved which puts the definition of the information system as a first priority out of which a variety of supporting techno- logical devices can be considered. Advanced technology demands that the methods of information systems development be as advanced as the technology itself and, therefore, the thinking that has dominated IT since the 1970s data-processing era is no longer relevant to current information systems.

AIM OF THIS TEXT

The view taken in this book is that an information system is the product of social interaction between human groups; it is a vehicle for communication which enables and supports the management of a business organization. The technological support that may be employed to enhance this interaction is considered within the context of the defined information system itself. Subsequently, this book is devoted to those methods, techniques and methodologies that will help the information systems profes- sional, together with the clients, to identify those information systems and technologi- cal devices that may be useful to them.

This text is directed towards the activities and responsibilities of the information systems professional and, in particular, those essential activities that precede the specification of technology—namely, the appreciation of the problem situation and the analysis and identification of the relevant information system(s). It is not the intention to advocate the use of one particular technique but rather to offer a philosophy of approach to act as a framework through which the ISA can facilitate the clients' specification of any particular information requirements. By 'clients' we refer to all those individuals, and groups, who have an interest in the definition and subsequent development of a specific information system. We do not seek to differentiate between client types as this makes no significant contribution to the ideas embodied within the interpretivist notions of CLD. Client-led design encapsulates the idea that the clients lead and control the information system definition. We have deliberately avoided labels such as 'user centred' or 'user participation' (Lucas, 1974; Robey and Farrow, 1982; Oppelland and Kolf, 1980; Straub and Trower, 1988) since we are advocating putting the clients in control of the whole information systems development process rather than just as participants.

The five-phase information system development process as provided through CLD will be addressed in the following way: Phase I, which we consider to be the cornerstone of the notion of CLD, is explored through a discussion of the concept upon which we base our approach, followed by a description of a variety of 'tools' considered to be appropriate in aiding both clients and practitioners in increasing their awareness of their problem situation. This will be followed by the problem identification and analysis activities of Phase I. We draw a distinction in Phase II between the identification of an information system and the technology that may be appropriate to it, and we turn our attention to the latter as a separate set of activities under Phase III. In Phase III, we then deal with the specification of appropriate technologies to satisfy the information system defined by the clients as a result of Phases I and II and their practical translation into a technology-supported information system. Phases IV and V relate to the implementation and subsequent maintenance and development activities involved in the information system design process as a whole.

Central to CLD is the notion of the role of the information systems analyst in enabling the clients to 'appreciate', define and specify their technology-based information system requirements. The aim of this text, therefore, is to provide an introduction to the kinds of skills and advanced methods of problem definition needed by the modern information systems professional. The text is suited to both undergraduate and postgraduate information systems students as well as to the information systems practitioner.

ACKNOWLEDGEMENTS

The development of this text has from time to time imposed itself upon colleagues and friends when advice or assistance was needed. Without exception this was given freely. Thanks are due to Richard Beeby, Malcolm Crowe, Jim Howell, Mark Stansfield and Richard Wilson for their comments on the text and for their lively and helpful discussion. A special thanks goes to Irene McKeown for her support throughout the writing of this text.

PART I

THE FOUNDATIONS OF CLIENT-LED DESIGN

INFORMATION SYSTEMS AND COMPUTING

INTRODUCTION

New thinking about technology-based information systems development requires that some fundamental assumptions about computing, data processing, information systems and the role of the information systems analyst be discussed. In this chapter we shall set out our philosophy of why it has been adopted and outline the concepts that are embedded in the general approach that we advocate.

COMPUTER SYSTEMS

In the 1970s many business enterprises had data processing (DP) departments whose prime function was to provide the company with specialist computer services. DP departments were usually under the administrative control of the company's finance department. Initially, the DP department's major task was to input and process data on the company's mainframe computer, primarily for the task of calculating employees' pay. As confidence grew in the use of the computer to process data, businesses began to apply its processing power to a number of other clerical tasks. A common feature of the kind of tasks in which a company computer may have been used were well understood by the management, and the tasks could be easily defined. During the 1980s and 1990s, as cheap, powerful and physically smaller computers became available, there has been a steady move towards their use in more complex areas of organizational activities: a move away from the relatively well-understood and easily identified activities of so-called number-crunching tasks into areas that are more difficult to define, such as management decision-making. This movement of computer application areas is illustrated in Figure 1.1.

The use of computing power has undoubtedly played a significant role in revitalizing many business enterprises but the application of computing to hitherto unimagined areas of business operations has led some critics to suggest that at times it is technology that seems to be defining business problems and their solution, and hence the frequent accusation that much of the new technology represents 'solutions looking for problems'.

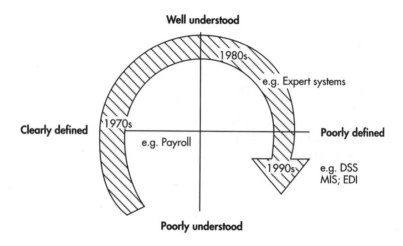

Figure 1.1 Trends in the use of computers in organizations

COMPUTER SYSTEMS AND INFORMATION SYSTEMS

In this book we make a clear distinction between a 'computer system' and an 'information system'. 'System' and 'information system' are dealt with in some detail in the following chapters but it is appropriate at this point to draw the reader's attention to the view we adopt about these two important aspects of information systems development.

In the literature and in common speech the term 'system' is frequently used as a synonym for a 'computer system'. Moreover, 'information system' is often assumed to mean a 'computer system'. However, in this text we draw a clear distinction between these words since the phrases 'computer system', 'information system' and 'technology-based information system' are used in distinct ways. A computer system refers to the grey box, a notional boundary drawn around the physical components, in which are contained the hardware and software of a computer system. An information system is concerned with the elements and activities of human communication involved in purposeful human activity. A technology-based information system is an information system in which a variety of technological devices are employed to improve the efficacy of the defined information system.

COMPUTER SYSTEMS ANALYST AND INFORMATION SYSTEMS ANALYST

One further distinction made within this text is that between a computer systems analyst (CSA) and an information systems analyst (ISA). The difference is as much an epistemological one as a reflection of the developments in IT. An ISA is concerned with the wider implications of information and the effects that an IT-based information system might have upon the organizational culture: the focus of attention is upon the decision-making processes involved in a human activity system (a notional system identified to highlight some purposeful human activity). The CSA, on the other hand, is concerned with the application of computers to the data-processing activities of the enterprise. This view is based upon the assumption that the data-processing activities are of essential importance to the improved performance of the enterprise. In general terms these two approaches correspond to Methlie's Infological and Datalogical definitions (Methlie, 1980).

The speed at which commercially available business computer systems have developed has meant that the design task has tended to become specialist and, consequently, increasingly technically biased (Nelson, 1986). The development of applications generators has increased the concentration of the analyst upon a specification that is compatible with the needs of the development tool (e.g. computer-aided software engineering; information engineering workstations). This reaction has often been at the expense of the amount of time and effort spent on the early process of problem 'appreciation'. It would appear that technological developments, particularly design tools, are seen by many practising CSAs as replacing the more 'time consuming' analytical methods (Benyon and Skidmore, 1987).

Most approaches to computer systems development apply techniques that can be described as quasi-scientific. These approaches are based upon the idea that the problem concerned can be quantified (or clearly specified) through the application of effective techniques to achieve specified ends. Such an approach stems from the apparent assumption that the most important objective is to provide a detailed technical specification for the purchase of hardware and software. Consequently, any organizational action is interpreted in a strictly instrumental fashion (Lyytinen and Klein, 1985). Such an objective can be accepted as being of fundamental importance for computer scientists, but when we are thinking about providing technical support for an information system it is more important that the definition of the information system should come first, followed by the identification and specification of the technology. In addition to technological knowledge, an understanding of organizational behaviour and cultural aspects is a substantive consideration in the information development process. Consequently, a more appropriate method of appreciation than is offered by those techniques that have been developed specifically to provide a technical specification, is required (Jayaratna, 1988). What we should not forget is that a computer is a tool that may facilitate improvements to information systems, intrinsically by means of the speed and accuracy with which it can process data. In a similar way a telephone system of communication provides a means of voice communication between remotely located individuals or groups. However, neither the computer nor the telephone can be accurately defined as an 'information system', although each makes an important contribution to a system's overall efficiency.

PHILOSOPHICAL FOUNDATIONS OF COMPUTER SYSTEMS METHODOLOGIES

The underlying concept of most computer system design methodologies is essentially reductionist and many of the information system design methods that have been developed were created to satisfy an operational need without regard to the philosophical underpinning of the ideas (Winograd and Flores, 1986). The result of this practical tradition has been a stream of tools/techniques/methods which are geared towards translating existing organizational operating procedures into a data specification. Once again, this practice emphasizes the tacit assumption that the company information needs can be satisfied by improving the efficiency of data-processing. Ideas about information systems analysis and design do not appear to have progressed very far over the past decade, and the mainframe payroll systems that were dominant in the 1970s still seem to persist in much of the work in the field of information systems. The computer systems design approaches presented in Table 1.1 are an attempt to show them in terms of their main features. If we use Methlie's broad definitions then we suggest that all the approaches shown would fall within the datalogical approach. As such these methods are inappropriate, as they stand, in satisfying what have become the requirements for modern organizational information systems definition. In the 1990s we require a philosophy that is more concerned about a variety of technologies (such as FAX, audio and teleconferencing facilities, duplicating machines, multimedia systems, and computing power of various types), which can aid and support the efficiency, efficacy and effectiveness of company information systems.

As we develop the notions of modern information systems analysis it soon becomes evident that the ISA requires more than just technical skills to orchestrate the development of an information system. The whole process of developing and designing a computer-aided information system necessitates the analyst intervening into the working practices and customs of an organization's culture, an activity that will almost certainly alter the way in which the organization operates and the way in which its social networks interact: their actions are effectively the catalysts of organizational change which go beyond the narrow confines of computer hardware and software.

MARKET PRESSURES

Growing competition in the business world and the need to adapt quickly to a changing environment has led to an increasing reliance of business enterprises upon the data-processing capacities of computer technology. Experience of introducing computers into organizations has awakened managers to the staff problems and the social changes engendered by the introduction of IT and of the need to carefully manage this change. Today's managers are aware of the only-too-often 'failure' of their computer-based information system to realize its full potential—a situation that has led researchers and managers to look for ways of improving the development and, hence, performance of the company's computer-based information system. New ideas about information systems design have included the need to address the management of change (e.g. the way in which the introduction of new technology affects working practices and procedures), organizational power, client involvement and the transfer of ownership of the developed information system from the consultant to the client. This change in emphasis in information systems design has also been reflected by some multinational IT manufacturers who, over the last few years, have switched emphasis from selling IT as the solution to business problems to that of marketing a 'solution' for business problems in which IT may play an important role. The emphasis has been placed upon investigating the 'problem' and then, if required by the client, recommending appropriate hardware and software to address the problem(s) identified. Finally, the speed of change in terms of the business environment and the technological progress of IT represents one more reason why greater emphasis should be placed upon the initial understanding and analysis of the problem situation than is the current practice.

DEFICIENCIES OF CURRENT INFORMATION SYSTEMS DESIGN METHODS

Information systems existed long before the invention of the microchip (Buckingham *et al.*, 1987), and yet information systems that have a computer at their heart are often considered, by both the lay person and the computer scientist, to be the exclusive province of technology. Non-computer scientists appear, until recently, to have paid little regard to the actual development procedures of computer-based data-processing systems. It is perhaps because of this that there are so few design approaches capable of taking into account the wider considerations involved in the generation and dissemination of information.

Table 1.1 shows the dates and prime concerns of some computer systems design methods that have been (and are being) used by CSAs over the past two decades. The dominant feature of each of the methods presented in the table is the definition of the requirements for the computer. None of the approaches seems to differentiate between a computer-based data-processing system and an information system. Instead, the assumption seems to be that the computer *is* the information system and, consequently, the definition of data and its associated flows is the most important factor. Where a methodology explicitly encourages client involvement, the client's role seems to be constrained largely to the identification of data-processing activities or

Table 1.1 History of computer systems design methods (after Stowell, 1991)

Year	Method	Feature	Activity
1969	Traditional (e.g. NCC)	Systems life cycle	Data definition and technical specification
1979	Structured systems analysis	Logical model of processes	Data flow of overall system
1979	Participative approach	Consultative, representative consensus participation	Design of human and technical part of computer system
1979	Information engineering	Normalized logical data structure	Data definition
1981	Information engineering	Strategic planning of information system	
1981	Jackson system development	Production of maintainable systems	Modelling of entity life histories as sequential processes
1983	Prototyping	Client and analyst develop a 'system' model using prototyping software	Client involvement in data definition
1989	Information systems engineering	Creation of a data dictionary/encyclopedia	Analysis of company strategy in data terms as the basis for information engineering workbench
1984–90	Structured systems analysis and design method	Data and process modelling	Data analysis, definition and technical specification
1985–90	Multiview	Computer system development as a hybrid process	Rationalization of client views as the basis of data definition
1991	Object-oriented analysis	Software systems as cooperating objects	Examines requirements from perspective of the classes of objects found in the vocabulary of the problem domain (Booch 1991)

to discussions about the way in which the computer might be used to improve efficiency. It is misleading to say that these methods were not developed with the intention of being used as problem identification tools since, in *practice,* they are often used in this way. However, the methodologies highlighted in Table 1.1 can be criticized in terms of their apparent lack of concern with the identification of the 'problem situation' and subsequent failure to address the situation in any way other than that which is appropriate to the installation of a computer. Notwithstanding the fact that these tools make no pretensions about being methods of problem investigation, they are often used in this way due to a lack of alternative tools or approaches. (Perhaps the notable exception to this criticism is 'object-oriented analysis' which, potentially, offers a link to the kind of information system definition approaches we advocate within this text.)

Using computer systems analysis methods as problem-solving tools means that the definition of the problem situation is directly related to the needs of the computer which, in itself, results in the context of the problem situation being minimized in favour of data definition. Within this scenario the role of the client during the information system design process has attracted the attention of some researchers and practitioners, and ways of optimizing their input to the design process have been considered as a means of validating the analysis process. However, despite such attempts to embrace the social aspects of an information system the practice of even the more socially oriented methods still seem to be based upon a functional and technical concept of information systems. (A similar view is expressed about socio-technical system approaches by Lyytinen and Klein, 1985.)

From Table 1.1 it appears that the analytical and design tools that are most commonly used by CSAs concentrate on the technical aspects of the perceived situation (Miles, 1985). The prime reason for this appears to be that the methods employed for the design and development of computer systems have been developed out of what Winograd and Flores (1986) call the 'rationalistic tradition' and to what Hirschheim (1985) describes as the 'positivist' view. Winograd and Flores (1986) refer to the 'tradition of rationalism and logical empiricism' as the underlying philosophy from which computing has been developed, an origin hardly surprising since from an early age we are taught that the rationalistic tradition, with the prestige and success it has received through scientific method, has become synonymous with 'what it means to think and be intelligent'. It is easy to understand, therefore, how computing has developed within this successful theoretical stance. However, the work of researchers such as Winograd and Flores serves (a) to remind us that we should critically evaluate the appropriateness of adopting the rationalistic tradition without question in information systems work, and (b) to encourage us to seek alternative approaches that may be beneficial. By adopting a 'rationalistic' or 'positivist' stance to information systems we are basing our work on the assumption that it is possible to dismantle and then quantify an information system to enable it to be reconstructed in computer form. Such an inculcated view might enable us to build a successful computer data-processing system but, we believe, it will not support the identification and development of computer-based information systems.

A further problem area with the development of computer-based information systems can be linked to what Churchman (1971) refers to as the problem of 'generality'. In practice, the CSA's preference to resurrect previous ideas as a quick route forward (created in part by the design procedure adopted by CSAs) is often precipitated by the pressure to save on pre-design time. In this way, as a means of avoiding unnecessary analysis and design effort, the CSA, when faced with what is perceived to be a similar problem to that experienced in a past project, re-uses ideas and solutions, and effectively regurgitates what we might call 'off-the-shelf solutions'. By its very nature, this approach means that scant regard is paid to the more individual and social aspects, such as the culture of the enterprise itself. An argument against 'generality' is that if each information system is unique to those involved, as well as being unique to each business enterprise, then each information system definition can be expected to be unique also — a solution to a problem in one place should not be expected to be a solution to a seemingly similar problem in a different setting.

Similarly to the problem of 'generality' outlined above, it is not unusual for the analyst to favour one analytical approach over another, possibly because of past success in using the method or perhaps because it is the most popular. For example, Structured Systems Analysis and Design Method (SSADM) is currently the most commonly used method of computer system development, presumably because in addition to successes that may have resulted from its use, it has been made 'respectable' by its formal teaching and assessment through official SSADM training courses and government backing. However, many SSADM users fully recognize its weaknesses and are seeking solutions to those problems. The tendency to use popular methods has many advantages, such as quality control of the application of the method, but there is also the danger that an approach may become institutionalized and may effectively limit thinking. The problem solver needs to be at liberty (intellectually as well as practically) to be able to select a method because it is the most appropriate for the task rather than because it is the most popular. Of equal importance to the competent use of a method of analysis is that the practitioner should be able to make a critical evaluation of the variety of methods available. By thinking about methods of analysis and the models of the problem situation that may consequently occur, the practitioner may reduce the possibility of bias that the habitual use of one method may engender.

THINKING ABOUT INFORMATION SYSTEMS

A popular conception of an information system supposes that information systems can be represented in a computer form and that 'information' and 'data' are interchangeable terms which represent something readily definable by an observer. Indeed, one dictionary of computers states 'information system: a general term to denote all the operations and procedures involved in a data processing system; i.e. including all clerical operations and communications methods used with the organization concerned' (Penguin Dictionary, 1985 edn.). This description of an information system does not coincide with the view taken in this text, so we must make our standpoint clear by explaining our understanding of the notion of an information system. In order to do this we must spend some time discussing the two concepts involved: 'information' and 'system'.

WHAT IS INFORMATION?

Information is defined in one dictionary as 'intelligence given: knowledge' (Chambers Dictionary, 1990 edn.) and, in the same dictionary, 'information science' is defined as 'the study of processing and communication of data, especially by means of computerized systems'. Another dictionary provides the definition: '(1) knowledge acquired through experience or study' and later in the list of definitions, '(6) Computer (a) the meaning given to data by the way it is interpreted; (b) same as data' (Collins Dictionary, 1992 edn.). The dictionary that is accessible in the word-processing package on which this chapter is being typed defines information as: 'that which is known; the sum of what has been perceived, discovered, or inferred'. In everyday speech the word information is commonly misused, with the words 'data' and 'information' being used interchangeably.

In the first definition quoted above there seems to be a clear implication that 'information' contains intelligence; that is to say, it concerns knowledge about a specific subject (or perhaps knowledge attributed to that subject). The second definition appears to share a similar perception in that there is within it an implication about 'knowing' that would suggest, by its very nature as a conscious activity, some human involvement in the process. However, the definition given for 'information science' compounds the problem in that it is placed squarely in the domain of data and computers. In this instance does the definition mean that a data-processing and communication system is the same as an information system? It would seem that computing has established its own meanings upon language which, in a sense, have corrupted and confused our understanding of these terms.

A further complication surrounding the definition of 'information' lies in the fact that the definition quoted above for 'information science' includes the words

'...computerized system', which leaves the reader with questions about the type of system that is being computerized. We shall return to the ill-use of the word 'system' later, but first let us consider the problems involved in defining information by thinking about 'data' and 'meaning'.

Data and meaning

The following is a simple example to illustrate the difficulties of defining information. If we are confronted with a random cluster of symbols such as that shown in Figure 1.2, it is most likely that this will be meaningless to most readers since there does not seem to be a recognizable pattern.

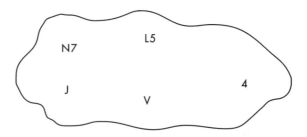

Figure 1.2   Random cluster

If we rearrange this cluster of letters and numbers into boxes, as shown in Figure 1.3, the reader may well begin to attribute meaning to it.

LJ	N7	45V

Figure 1.3.   Boxed

We need to ask ourselves, however, if this rearrangement helps us to imply meaning? If it does, what is the meaning that you, the reader, have attributed to this cluster of letters and numbers and, perhaps more importantly, where did your meaning come from? It is likely that our experience of seeking meaning through patterns may suggest a pattern that is meaningful to us personally, such as a membership number or an account number. On the other hand, if you are unable to attribute a meaning to this cluster then how would you describe what you are looking at? If the boundary is removed from the cluster and it is presented as a series of letters and numbers, as shown in Figure 1.4, it may be possible to attribute meaning to it, but if so, where did this meaning come from?

Figure 1.4   Series

Let us develop this idea by arranging the cluster into a more recognizable pattern, as shown in Figure 1.5.

LJN 745V

Figure 1.5   Final grouping of symbols

No doubt some readers (in the UK at least) will have formed an opinion about what they are looking at and conclude that it could be a UK vehicle registration number. Let us consider what has been done. By moving the symbols into a particular arrangement it has been possible to convey meaning despite the fact that the arrangement of the letters and numbers themselves make no sense in the English language. Further meaning may be attributed incorrectly in a sudden recognition of this pattern of numbers and letters. For example, most of those who recognize the arrangement of symbols will describe it as automobile registration number. It will rarely occurs to them that it could just as easily be the registration number of a motor-cycle or a bus. Although apparently trivial, this assumption raises two important points that illustrate the delicacy of the way in which we attribute meaning to data: (a) is the assumption that is being made by the reader just a figure of speech in which 'automobile registration number' was a generic phrase for 'vehicle registration plate' or, (b) did he or she really mean an auto registration plate and hence have made a correct assumption?

To take this example further, if we assume that the cluster of letters and numbers does in fact represent the registration plate of a motor-car we can conjecture that there are a number of people for whom the registration means more than just a number (see Figure 1.6). For example, the original salesperson who sold the vehicle will know what the sale meant in terms of income to the business and possibly what bonus it attracted (e.g. the sale of this automobile may have paid for the salesperson's summer vacation). The automobile engineer who serviced the vehicle may recognize the registration and associate the technical problems that this vehicle represented. The owner, of course, can provide many more intimate details. We may have a professional interest in this registration plate as a police officer or a breakdown recovery service. For example, if necessary, a police officer can identify the geographical area from which the plate was registered and it may be possible to identify the dealer to whom the number was assigned and, therefore, connect the plate with a particular model and/or make of car. The breakdown recovery service would use the registration as a means of identifying the vehicle and, through that, the owner and his or her credentials (e.g. membership) and may use it as a method of identifying, through the date of registration contained in British plates, the model and mark of the vehicle and thereby the details of any replacement parts necessary.

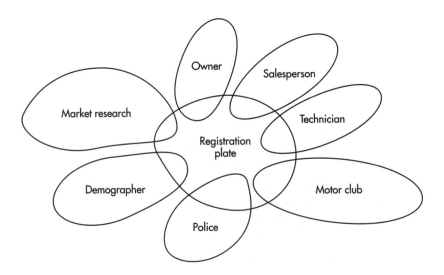

Figure 1.6   Different parties that may attribute a particular meaning from the data represented by a vehicle registration plate

A registration plate can sometimes be a status symbol (e.g. a personalized number plate) and the year suffix or prefix may be taken as representing the financial and personal status of its owner. Some marketing programmes, or market researchers, may use car registration plates as demographic indicators concerning the distribution of wealth (e.g. the number of newly registered vehicles). Clearly the wealth of information which surrounds the registration plate is considerable but it is the *context* that each of the parties identified above brings to the situation that allows them to make sense of and attribute 'meaning' to the data represented by the numbers and letters of the registration plate.

Using this example of the vehicle registration plate can help to answer some difficult questions, such as, 'At what point does data become information?' and 'Is the information itself the same for all concerned?' This commonplace illustration of the information that can be extracted from a 7-character set of data is a powerful example of the way in which information is dependent not only upon the context in which it is used but also on the interests (or 'readinesses' in the Vickerian sense (Vickers, 1984)) of the information receiver concerned with attributing meaning to the data provided. Hopefully, this example highlights that key factors in this 'meaning-attribution' activity are the human being and the context in which that person is functioning.

WHAT IS A SYSTEM?

Let us now consider the definition and use of the word 'system'. Common parlance suggests that the word 'System' has a variety of meanings, each inspired by the context in which the term is used. The careful listener will soon discover the varied usage of the word, with different meanings emerging depending upon context. For example, people refer to a system as a way of doing something (office procedures; a filing system; an accounting system). The sense of the meaning here seems to imply a systematic approach to a particular set of activities. But one could ask: Is there an accounting system that is identical in every way in every business enterprise? In this ill-considered use of the word system, an assumption is made (or perhaps ignored) that while the accounting system being referred to by the speaker has certain common characteristics that enable it to be classified as an accounting *system* there are other aspects that make it unique. An accounting system can be said to have certain common properties, but to gain understanding about a particular company's accounting system requires not only an understanding of the elements that make it up but also an appreciation of the context in which that accounting system resides. (There are a number of important elements to the problems of context, which will be discussed in Chapters 2 and 3.)

Another example of the use of the term 'system' is the frequent reference to a mystical intelligence somehow controlling events. For example, one hears reference to 'it's the system' as a means of explaining an effect or the way that something is done which is outside the speaker's control and, perhaps, understanding. The term is sometimes used as a substitute for 'The Establishment', with the constraints and limitations that society places upon individuals or an event that the speaker considers to be the architect of something unpalatable undermining his or her aspirations (e.g. health, education, social welfare). The term 'system' is frequently used as a name for some tangible entity that has an intelligence of its own and is recognized by all concerned. Take, for example, a not uncommon complaint that a benefit (financial or otherwise) has not been forthcoming because of the machinations of the system. The system is not defined and the speaker assumes that the listener knows the cause of the complaint. However, it is quite likely that the listener will make his or her own assumptions about the object of complaint and enter into the conversation without the actual object ever being defined. 'System' is also used repeatedly to define any piece of technology (e.g. hi-fi, photographic equipment) and even items such as washing powders, soap dispensers and decongestants. However, the word is probably most commonly used when referring to a computer, or linked network of computers (e.g. 'It's a good system' or 'The system is down again', or 'What system has your company installed?' or 'It's the system's fault'). Moreover, the meaning of the word 'system' in this context has been supported by a popular misunderstanding of the title 'systems analyst' as a reference to those who design 'computer systems' or 'systems'.

The diverse use of the word 'system' has been discussed by Checkland (Checkland and Scholes, 1990) who has suggested that the term is so badly used that we should concede the word to popular usage and adopt, instead, Koestler's word 'holon' as a specialist word to describe the assembly of activities that form the basis of our interest (Koestler, 1967; Checkland, 1988). However, trying to implement the word 'holon' does result in some rather awkward descriptions and so in this text we shall continue to talk about systems, but in doing so we adopt a particular meaning of the word, which is discussed below.

Apart from the wide usage of the word 'system' discussed above, a system, to 'systems thinkers', has a very particular meaning which involves a description of some collection of parts which, when connected together in a specific way, can be said to bring about some purposeful activity. While it is difficult to define exactly what a system is, Schoderbek *et al.* (1990) offer a relatively informed and informing definition which we shall use here:

> ...a *set* of *objects* together with *relationships* between the objects and between their *attributes* related to each other and to their *environment* so as to form a *whole*.

Systems thinking as an underpinning philosophy for information systems

Some commentators suggest that information systems have failed to become a discipline because practitioners recognize that the systems only form the delivery of a technical system (Lyytinen and Klein, 1985). Like these commentators we also believe that information systems require a philosophical grounding if they are to be anything more than a set of craft skills to develop computer-based information systems. We suggest that 'systems *thinking*' might provide the underpinning philosophy for information systems while 'systems *practice*' offers a variety of practical tools that will help in the development of computer-based information systems. In this way systems ideas can provide help in the process of information systems development both in terms of facilitating an holistic appreciation of the problem situation and by providing tools which enable that appreciation to be translated into a practical form. In short, the approach to problem-solving offered by systems thinking provides a suitable way of contemplating a problem without technical bias but at the same time, as will be shown in the following chapters, provides the practitioner with the means of translating the relevant elements of the investigation into a technological specification at the appropriate point in the study.

It is not the intention to provide either a detailed history of systems thinking within this text or a résumé of current thinking since these aspects are suitably covered in a wealth of books and papers elsewhere (e.g. Churchman, 1968; Ackoff, 1974; Checkland, 1981; Checkland and Scholes, 1990; Jackson, 1992). Instead, our aim is to provide a short discussion of the 'systems' way of thinking and, in the following chapter, to expand upon this and provide examples of the tools that are available and are deemed helpful in the process of, first, identifying and, then, defining information systems.

Reductionism versus holism
An examination of our everyday world reveals a complex domain of interrelated parts too difficult for us to cope with easily all at once. In our attempt to manage such complexity we reduce it to a form that we more readily be examined. A practical manifestation of this strategy is that as our civilization has evolved, so too have different areas of specialism. Our common perception of education and its 'disciplines' reflect this tendency towards compartmentalization and, as such, it is often difficult to remember that the divisions therein are arbitrary: physics, biology, psychology, sociology and engineering are not natural divisions (that exist externally to humanity's consciousness) but are the results of humanity's attempt to organize and make sense of the world that is perceived (Checkland, 1981). Because we have been educated in a particular way for such a long time these divisions have become ingrained into our thinking, which makes it difficult to see past them to the unity that underlies these artificial divisions. The danger is that we begin to imagine the world to *be* as our chosen discipline of learning describes it.

Computing science offers a clear example of the practice of dividing the world into even smaller parts as the means of handling complexity. Many systems analysis and design methods are concerned with reducing the situation down into its constituent parts to enable appropriate software to be written for the various parts which, when reassembled, will form the whole.

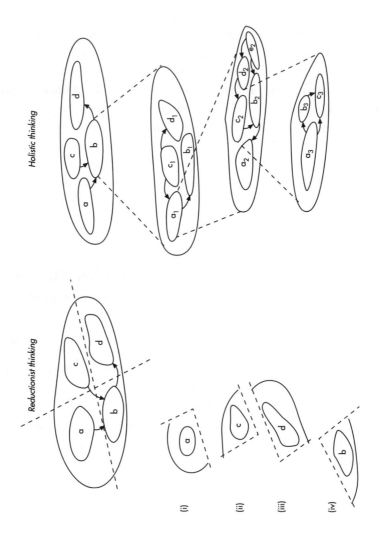

Figure 1.7   Reductionist and holistic thinking

'Systems', then, is a meta-discipline through which we can learn to think about prob-lem situations from a holistic perspective. It is important, however, that we regard 'systems' as a particular way of *thinking* which we may adopt to try to make sense of our world (Checkland, 1990)—it does not purport to give us the right answer at the end of the study, but only helps us manage our investigative, analytic and design process. Figure 1.7 serves to illustrate the difference between reductionist and holistic thinking.

While systems thinking may offer us a strong and useful foundation for thinking about information systems, it is vital that theory is not its only contribution but that it also offers something to practise. Fortunately, systems theory has been translated into a variety of practical systemic problem-solving methods and tools that offer the ISA a rich collection of practical tools for organizational intervention and interaction. Figure 1.8 illustrates how systems practice has been developed out of systems thinking which, in turn, has enhanced and contributed to systems thinking.

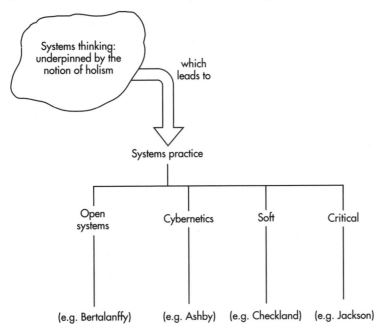

Figure 1.8   Systems theory and systems practice

The distinction between 'Hard' systems thinking and 'Soft' systems thinking
The formalization of systems thinking stems from the 1940s when researchers and practitioners from a wide range of subject areas sought to investigate and develop a meta-discipline for problem-solving. Within systems thinking it is possible to isolate two distinct streams of thought. The first and perhaps 'classical' consideration of

'system' relates to the assumption that systems *exist* as complex entities in the real world and as such can be identified and investigated. This view of 'systems' is often embodied in what is referred to as 'hard' systems thinking. The second view of 'system' is as a *notional* whole which may, or may not, have any substance in the real world: it is purely an intellectual construct. In this latter development of systems thinking, 'system' is taken as a particular way of *thinking* about our perceived world from which we may, if *we* wish and if *we* feel it may be useful, identify elements that *we may choose to view as a system* in order to make sense of our perceived world. Therefore, this second understanding of 'system' places great emphasis upon (a) the careful naming of the connected elements we choose to investigate as 'systems' and (b) the use of systems thinking as a tool in our enquiring and analytic processes. In this second view of 'system' it is important to realize that the understanding and definition of any system is dependent upon the view and intention of the one naming the system. The distinction between the two modes of systems thought is illustrated in Figure 1.9.

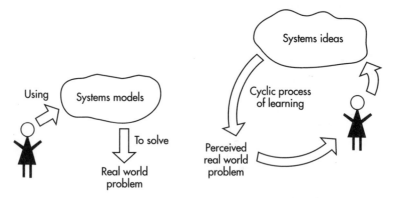

Figure 1.9   Two views of systems thinking

The distinction between the two modes of systems thinking has important implications for systems practice: while the 'classical' stance can be expected to model real world systems so as to optimize their performance, those using 'system' as a notional construct will use systems thinking as a means of *learning* about the perceived real world.

In order to capitalize on the doubtless strengths of systems ideas the practitioner, as a fundamental step towards intellectual awareness, should be aware of his or her own interpretation of the concept of a 'system'. For example, in the first case a system may be perceived as having easily definable physical characteristics, e.g. a central heating system; such a system includes a source of heating, storage, distribution and regulation but this same system also involves wider considerations, including a source of energy, space availability and aesthetic considerations. This concept of systems has an important practical value in that the system can be defined and its component parts 'identi-fied' in such a way as to be useful practically. In the second case, however, a central heating system might be identified as a system to provide a comfortable temperature in which people can exist in shirtsleeves, or a system to provide an environment to promote the growth of tomatoes.

The difference between the two views belies an important difference in the thinking about systems as a concept. In the first example the implication is that the system exists to be defined. In the second example there is a tacit acceptance that a system may be defined in a way that may aid *understanding* of the problem and its context but is perceived as a *notional* system. In this case, as the system practitioner's awareness increases, the definition of the system may change to reflect his or her interest. A perceived system is one that we chose to name through the selection of a set of relationships which seem meaningful to the practitioner as a whole at a given moment in time and will change as the practitioner's awareness increases through time. While the notional system is of use to us we may then define it as a system, but at the same time we recognize that its usefulness is limited by our worldview, our readiness to perceive and value, and our role as the enquirer. It is this second mode of systemic thought that we feel can make a major contribution both to the attempt to provide a theoretical basis for information systems and to the practical requirements of the information systems provision process.

INFORMATION SYSTEM: A DEFINITION

Given our new understanding of the words 'information' and 'system', we need to reflect upon the meaning of the term 'information system'. There are a number of ways to look at information. For example, Schoderbek *et al.* (1990) suggest that: 'In-formation refers to inferentially intended material evaluated for a particular problem, for a specified individual, at a specific time, and for achieving a definite goal.' Van Gigch (1988) attempts to extend the notion of information by his suggestion that there is a difference between data, information and intelligence. He argues that infor-mation is a subset of data in the form of knowledge and intelligence a subset of information used for decision-making or any form of action. Both definitions refer to, or imply, a process of selection from a source of data by a person for a specific purpose. Although van Gigch proposes data as being stimuli in the form of signals that enter the cognitive processes, there is a tenuous implication of a hierarchical relation-ship between information and intelligence.

Both Schoderbek and van Gigch highlight the process by which data is utilized by an individual or by a group within the context of their operational needs. However, neither satisfactorily defines an information system. They do, however, highlight the difference between data and information and, more importantly, draw our attention to the problem of differentiating between data that is useful and data that is not.

For the purposes of this text we offer the following as the definition of an information system:

> *An information system can be taken to be the notional whole through which the provision, manipulation and use of appropriate data to enable decision-making to take place is managed.*

While this definition does not presuppose the role of computers, it does take as given the role of the individual in assigning value and use to data and, hence, the transformation of this data into information.

THE NEED FOR CLIENT-LED DESIGN

In the foregoing sections we have set out the arguments for the need to review our ways of developing computer-based information systems. There would seem to be four main points to consider:

(1) An organization's information systems are difficult to define since although much organizational data may be shared, its interpretation and use by different organizational members may be varied.

(2) Most of the popular methods of developing computer-based information systems are designed around the desire to produce a technological solution to a problem situation. This situation is understandable since technology has been the driving force behind the development of these methods. The root cause of the problem, we suggest, relates to the absence of a strong underlying theory of information systems. Instead, methods of problem-solving have arisen out of approaches from the past which were developed for the express purpose of translating company activities into a form that could be data-processed.

(3) The flexibility that is offered by modern information technology and current thinking about information systems proposes that an organization should be considered not as a data-processing system but in terms of the *information systems* which enable it to function. A general characteristic of these information systems is that they are part of the organization's 'culture' and are a mixture of hard operational needs and soft social communication channels; therefore, any definition of an organizational information system should take into account these two intertwined elements.

(4) Introducing technology into an enterprise creates a disturbance which may engender a feeling of insecurity in those most affected. This feeling of insecurity

may result in a resistance to change which, in turn, may reduce the effectiveness of the technology.

One way to address the problems of information systems development is to transfer to the clients the ownership and 'responsibility' for addressing the problem and subsequent development and implementation of the solution. This belief has led to the development of a framework to support the 'client-*led*' design of computer-based information systems. It is important to stress that the word 'design' is used in its widest sense to cover the activities of investigating, analysing, defining, designing and implementing. The term 'client-led' has been chosen to emphasize that *the clients* are in control of the design process: the ISA, on the other hand, provides the clients with the methodologies, tools and techniques necessary to manage and control this process. This notion of 'client-*led*' is significantly different to that of 'client-*centred*' where the emphasis is upon placing the clients in the 'consultative' role rather than in the 'prescribing, directing, managing and controlling' role.

A further point that needs to be stressed before moving on to more practical issues is that although this text provides a five-phase approach which is referred to as a 'method for client-led design', what is illustrated should be seen clearly as representing *one* means of putting into practice the notion, or philosophy, of client-led design.

In the next chapter we expand upon the notion of 'system' and discuss some ideas of value to the ISA, which operationalize the systems concept.

REVIEW QUESTIONS

As one means of revising the essence of this chapter we provide the following key words. State what you now understand by the following:

- Data
- Data-processing
- Computer system
- Computer systems analyst
- Systems analyst
- System
- Information
- Information system
- Information systems analyst
- Client-led design
- Client-centred design

EXERCISES

(1) Explain three different views about the advantages and disadvantages of a FAX machine (e.g. an employer, an employee and a customer). From your list identify those views that coincide and those that do not.

(2) Assume that you are working within a personnel office and your role is to interview staff as part of their annual career review. In the execution of your role, identify those activities that you feel could be assisted by IT and those that you feel would be better left to the individual.

(3) From your understanding of human groups (say a hill-walking club) list all the elements that you feel are relevant to the information system that enables the group to function as a club.

2

SYSTEMS THINKING AS A BASIS FOR CLIENT-LED DESIGN

INTRODUCTION

In the previous chapter we discussed the nature of information systems and introduced the notion of systems thinking. One of our conclusions was that information systems are better defined by the individual or group within the client organization that has some reason to view a particular set of data as information. If we continue along this line of thought, then the roles of both the ISA and the 'clients' (or 'user'), need to be re-evaluated: instead of being the external agent who is responsible for analysing the organization's information requirements and prescribing a technical solution, the role of the ISA becomes one of *enabling* those who will use the information system, and who work as part of it, to define *their* information system and, consequently, the type of information technology required to support it. This is not to assume that the technical knowledge of the ISA becomes redundant; on the contrary, up-to-date knowledge of technology and its strengths and limitations is vital if the requirements established by the clients are to be translated into a good and appropriate technological solution. However, in addition to this technical knowledge the ISA requires other skills, tools and methods to aid in the client-led design process and it is to these extra requirements that the following chapters are addressed. The difference between the roles of the ISA and what has been traditionally referred to as the systems analyst is illustrated in Figure 2.1.

CONTEXTUAL ISSUES: ORGANISATIONAL CULTURE

In order for the ISA to enable the clients to articulate their information system requirements it is important that the clients' awareness of the problem situation does not stop at their own particular area of interest but is extended to cover the whole problem situation. Furthermore, the ISA needs to gain an appreciation of the whole problem situation if the advice given is to be of value to the clients. It is difficult to try to view a situation from another's perspective, and the situation is made more complex by the need to recognize the context in which an information system exists.

Data processing   Information system

Figure 2.1   The role of the computer systems analyst and the information systems analyst

This includes the need for an 'outsider' (which is often what the ISA is) to consider such an intangible idea as that of organizational 'culture' since the complex combination of factors that are collectively referred to as making up the 'culture' of an organization is likely to determine the way in which the project proceeds and, so, dictate its future success or failure.

Organizational culture is difficult to discuss objectively, especially if one is not part of the organization under investigation. Much literature exists which discusses a variety of concepts and approaches regarding this subject area (e.g. Emery and Trist, 1960; Katz and Kahn, 1966; Albrow, 1973; Handy, 1976; Pfeffer, 1981; Blackler and Shimmin, 1984; Mintzberg, 1984; Pugh *et al.*, 1985; Flood and Carson, 1988). It is not the intention in this chapter to discuss these works but merely to emphasize the need to be aware of the complexity of an organization's 'culture' and its significance for the development of information systems. Even being a member of an organization does not always mean that it is easy to define that organization's 'culture'. For example, an organization may be recognized by its members to have a culture which places great emphasis upon caring for its staff and ensuring that they receive first-class training since the organization recognizes that well-trained staff are more likely to react positively in their work. An alternative culture might be one in which organizational members always rise to the occasion—all pulling together in times of need. An organization may have a culture that is highly formalized, in which all management decision-making is strictly hierarchical, or a culture in which decisions are made informally. In short, the market in which an organization operates, the early origins of the business, or the personalities of staff may all play a part in helping to form the culture of that organization.

The importance and strength of organizational culture and the results of ignoring it can be illustrated in an example of one large UK business enterprise. The organization in question has its origins in the early history of passenger transportation when courtesy and the notion of being a 'member' of a special club were of utmost importance. The organizational culture that evolved over the years was one of a 'members' club' that took care of its employees. However, an economic recession affected the profitability of the company and new senior management were introduced to 'shake things up'. These managers, who were not part of those helping to maintain the culture, made many changes and introduced new practices that were inconsistent with the strong, original organizational culture. A difficult period followed; the many changes that were implemented resulted in a significant number of management personnel leaving the company and a new 'uneasy' culture was imposed upon the organization. The change of management ethos may, in turn, affect the customer and create other types of problems which, in turn, may alter the emergent property of the enterprise. For example, a members' club may be characterized by a caring management who put the wishes of the members first, but change the management to one whose prime motivation is to make a profit at any cost and they may become remote from the members they are supposed to serve.

The above example serves to show how an organization that is characterized by an ethos of caring and a community spirit may be endangered by the new goals of profit maximization and efficiency. Alternatively, the culture of an enterprise may evolve which is to the disadvantage of those who work within it. For example, the ethos, or culture, of the business organization may be one in which there is antagonism towards any form of change. The mining and print industries may be seen as examples of the type of industrial strife that may be generated as a result of challenging what appears to be outmoded or inappropriate organizational culture (Emery and Trist, 1960; Ashworth, 1986; Stowell, 1989). In these cases there was a general feeling from the workforce that the management had little concern for the well-being of their employees and on the management side there was an impression that the necessary modernization of the industries was being prohibited by outmoded traditions and working practices. In the case of the print dispute the culture of the industry was such that the unions' claim that their members were being harshly treated by the newspaper management found little public support (Stowell, 1989). The end result of this situation was, and still is to some degree, poor industrial relations, mistrust and a general lack of willingness to contemplate change.

However, taking care to work within and preserve a particular organizational culture can be used to advantage. For example, the traditional working practices and standards of specialist hand–built sport cars has succeeded in marketing this unique organizational culture as an advantage—e.g. Morgan—to one sector of the motor-car production industry. The Morgan is valued by customers who seem to be more concerned with the uniqueness of their purchase and with the quality associated with traditional skill than with the latest technology but 'sameness' of mass-produced vehicles.

The culture that emerges from the interaction between individuals and groups within an enterprise plays an important role in forming the character or culture of the organization and, hence, any attempt to change the culture, whether intentional or otherwise, may be expected to have a considerable effect on the business and its employees. For the ISA, an important question must then be something in the form of: 'How will the introduction of information technology to support these information systems affect and be affected by the culture of this organization/department?' Potential areas of change that may affect the organizational culture include such areas as working procedures and practices, responsibilities held, structures, lines of authority and social grouping (Stowell, 1989).

Given that the ISA is able to gain some appreciation of the organization's culture, it is important to recognize that such an appreciation may not necessarily reflect the perceptions of those within the organization. Similarly, one employee's perception may be different to another's while different interpretations of the dominant culture may develop in various departments, or between branches of the organization. It is the recognition of the importance of such complex and inherently subjective areas as 'organizational culture' that emphasizes the need to provide ISAs with the methodologies and tools that enable clients to explore and define their own information needs to meet *their* individual requirements as well as those of the organization as a whole. A prime task for the ISA is to understand the organizational context in which the technology is to be installed.

THE MANAGEMENT OF CHANGE

Information technology (IT) is often referred to as a 'catalyst for change' since, on recognizing that business outputs need to be improved, IT is often the vehicle through which this improvement is sought (e.g. Rzevski, 1988). Increasingly, it becomes evident that the business world is in a constant state of change and that a business organization needs to be able to respond to changes in its environment quickly and appropriately (Stowell, 1989). This need can be met by the speed and accuracy with which data can be gathered, processed and acted upon by the organizational members using IT. However, the introduction of any new technology brings about changes to many different areas of concern—for example, the organization's structure, and to its working practices and procedures, and the levels of responsibility held by individuals and groups which, in turn, alter the way in which power and resources are distributed throughout the organization.

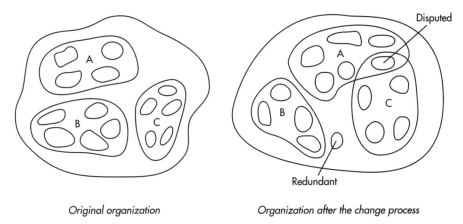

Original organization   Organization after the change process

Figure 2.2 IT and organizational change (after Wilson, 1982, and Parker-Follett—see Parker, 1984)

As illustrated in Figure 2.2, the change that the introduction of IT can bring affects the authority, operation and power relationships between groups. For example, the diagram on the right shows how, after the introduction of IT, the boundaries between each of the original groups has been shifted. This shift gives A more control and an increase in responsibilities, while group C loses one part of its domain and one of B's activities has become redundant. There is also one activity where the control is disputed. This diagram serves to show how changes that the introduction of IT can bring about can be expected to affect the way in which individuals undertake their jobs and may redefine their roles within the organization. The pressures, uncertainties, threats and opportunities which such changes represent can engender a resistance to change in those who are likely to be affected. Such resistance may show itself in a number of ways and many examples can be found, such as lack of cooperation, refusal to use the new information systems, sabotage, withdrawal of goodwill, and industrial action. Learning from such examples has led some practitioners to attempt to overcome the problem of resistance to change by variously involving those affected by the IT in its analysis, design and implementation. This philosophy has produced methodologies such as the participative approach (Mumford and Henshall, 1979), Multiview (Wood-Harper et al., 1985, Avison and Wood-Harper (1990), prototyping (Maude and Willis, 1991), and object-oriented design (Booch, 1991), all of which have claimed to have at their heart the participation of the clients. However, we have suggested in the previous chapter that these approaches do not go far enough towards providing a clear theoretical underpinning upon which to base a practical structure to support full client involvement. Instead, they seem to be primarily concerned with solving the problem and then providing an efficient technological solution to this problem. Traditionally, little attention has been paid to exploring and understanding the problem situation and more consideration has been given to analysis. Defenders of this approach argue that problem investigation is implicit in analysis, but when questioned about the tools used for this phase of the study we are confronted with questionnaires and references to unstructured interviews. In point of fact the role of the analyst has hitherto been primarily concerned with the identification and specification of a computer-based data-processing system as opposed to problem-solving in its widest sense, with the client acting in a consultative rather than in a monitoring and controlling role.

In many instances in the recent past so-called user-centred approaches have been used as a 'front end' to the more structured information system design methods. In practice, what has resulted is a variation on the traditional method of analysis in which the subjective element of the approach becomes subsumed by the practicalities of produc-ing a good IT-based information system, which has resulted in the wishes of the clients often being neglected due to the need to rationalize what has been learned in order to satisfy the technical specification.

Attempts to bridge the gap between the 'soft' problem situation analysis and the 'hard' technical specification has received considerable interest during the past few years (e.g. Stowell, 1985, 1991; Stowell et al., 1990; Miles, 1985, 1988; Prior, 1991, 1992; Wood, 1992; Doyle and Wood, 1991; Sawyer, 1992, Davies and Ledington, 1991). Researchers and practitioners have suggested various ways of linking these two areas, ranging from methods of embedding and grafting the two different approaches together to making several conscious paradigm shifts between the two areas and the use of a complex series of models to support this process. Little real evidence of the success of the approaches has been forthcoming and the exercise has fuelled re-searchers with criticisms and proposals. One way of attempting to overcome the bridging of the 'soft'/'hard' gap is to encourage and facilitate clients to identify and design their own information systems. In this way the analyst is not placed in the posi-tion of trying to interpret the problem situation and translate it into the most appro-priate technology-based information system. Instead, the aim is to enable each client to recognize and identify the areas in which technological support is appropriate. With this objective in mind we advocate that the process of designing the information system must be developed by the client together with the ISA in an advisory role throughout the five phases of the IS development process that was identified above. In each of the five phases of the development process (see Preface and Figure 2.3) the clients should determine what they consider to be the desirable outcomes of the

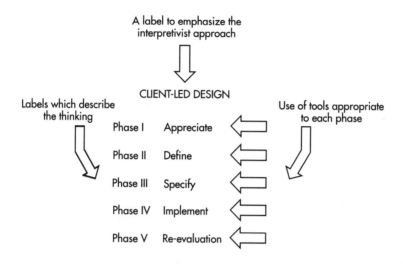

Figure 2.3   CLD as a framework for thinking about the IS development process

exercise. An important point is that the development of the information system should be considered in its widest context by both the ISA and the clients and not just as a set of discrete steps in which the definition of the information system is predominated by the wish to produce a specification for the technological devices.

A METHOD TO SUPPORT CLIENT-LED DESIGN

We have suggested two major areas of weakness in the process of information system design: (a) the lack of problem appreciation by the analyst and client, and (b) the failure to give the client the lead in the design of the technology-supported information system. We have proposed that one method of addressing this is to redefine the information system development process. In the Preface to this book we referred briefly to the proposed five phases of development of an information system that supports the argument for client-led design (CLD). In the remainder of this chapter we focus upon these five phases, the role of the ISA and systems thinking.

The five phases of client-led information system design should not be seen as mapping onto any proclaimed 'real world' stages or activities in the same way as the traditional, and arbitrary, CSA–created 'systems life cycle'. It must be emphasized that the pro-posed five phases are intended as a framework to support the practical application of tools and techniques that enable CLD to take place. It is *not* a formal method with a checklist of actions within a discrete set of steps embedded within clearly defined and structured stages. What we argue for here is a framework which the clients, the team, or stakeholders, may find useful in helping them to undertake and manage CLD, and as such can be seen as a set of processes that appear to be relevant to the development of technology-supported information systems. As a framework it should be seen by all involved as supporting an iterative process, and the starting point may be at any stage of the framework that is appropriate to the needs of the team. Figure 2.3 shows the thinking which CLD represents. Within the CLD framework a method or part of a method might be used if it is appropriate to the problem, e.g. soft systems methodology, object-oriented design, information engineering or specific tools such as brainstorming, root definitions, or data flow diagrams. It is important for the designer to remember that the design process needs to embrace all stages before action to install the technology is taken. Moreover, the framework itself should be seen as representing a never-ending cycle of learning in the manner of action research (action research is dealt with in more detail in Chapter 5). In the case of the technological input to the information system design process, action should only be taken when all parties agree that action is appropriate. Figure 2.4 illustrates the iterative nature of the framework for the CLD presented.

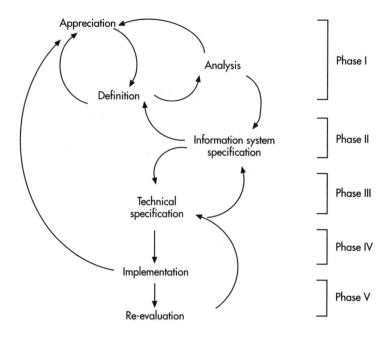

Figure 2.4   The iterative nature of the proposed framework for supporting CLD

The framework illustrated in Figure 2.4 provides a pictorial representation of the client-led design (CLD) process—a series of phases with the phases themselves being vehicles for 'packages' of ideas that will aid the process of expressing the information system need right through to the fulfilment of that expressed need. Within the framework the practitioner and client will use ideas and methods that are appropriate to the problem situation but, and this is most important, with respect to the philosophy upon which CLD is based, namely interpretivism. The phases of design should not be used as if they were stages in a technique. Each phase is intended to enable clients to express their needs and to enable them to reflect upon the relationship of each expression to each part of the process as a whole, and so the phases become an iterative cycle of events in which the clients define and agree to technology being implemented, updated, extended and replaced in a time-scale appropriate to their needs.

In the following pages we provide a description of each of the general actions that we would expect to take place within each of the evolutionary phases of CLD.

PHASE I

Phase I is the most important part of the framework in which the clients and the ISA gain an *appreciation* of the problem situation and of each other's perception of the problem. By appreciation we mean the learning process expressed by Vickers (1983) and by Checkland (1981). Appreciation involves both judgements of value and judgements of reality, a system which Vickers describes as manifesting itself in 'the exercise through time of mutually related judgements of reality and value' (Vickers, 1983, p. 67). He refers to this process as a system because each attribute appears to be part of the overall method used by individuals to make sense of what is observed. Appreciative judgements reflect the view held by an individual of a situation at a given point in time. 'Value' and 'reality' are not static but develop with each situational encounter. So, too, the ISA's preconception of a situation is modified by the knowledge gained from observations as an attempt is made to appreciate what is taking place. The development of the appreciative system is both enabling and inhibiting but is essentially the 'inner history of an individual, an organization and a society' (Vickers, 1983, p. 69).

Vickers suggests that individuals learn not only new valuations through experience but also increase their skill in valuing; and they learn these things by the activity of 'appreciation' (Vickers, 1983). This process is summarized by Checkland:

> Vickers (1970) argues that our human experience develops within
> us 'readiness to notice particular aspects of our situation, to discrimi-
> nate them in particular ways and to measure them against particular

standards of comparison, which have been built up in similar ways'. These readinesses are organised into 'an appreciative system' which creates for all of us, individually and socially, our appreciated world. The appreciative settings condition new experience, but are modified by the new experience; such circular relations Vickers takes to be the common facts of social life, but we fail to see this clearly, he argues, because of the concentration in our science-based culture on linear causal chains and on the notion of goal-seeking.

(Checkland, 1981, p. 263)

The prime purpose of Phase I, then, is for the participants to gain an understanding of the problem situation, including its information systems. We can call upon some simple ideas and tools (described later in this chapter and in the chapter that follows) that help to facilitate this process.

The success of Phase I is vital to the outcome of the project. If the task is a 'green field' project and the participants are unknown to each other, then the importance of this phase cannot be overemphasized; it is the foundation upon which the project is built. It is important that the ISA ensures that the client-set (that is, that proportion of clients directly affected by the problem situation) is representative of the problem situation and that the procedures adopted are not intimidating to junior members of the group. It may not be relevant or useful to use the traditional model of 'representative personnel' (e.g. managers, union representatives and staff) since the participants should be representatives from those members of staff who can contribute to the overall appreciation of the problem situation. Ideally, this would include all members of staff, but clearly this is not possible in some cases. It is important to stress that the closer the ISA can get to representing all views and to ensuring that all involved are acquainted with those views, then the fewer difficulties are likely to be encountered at later stages in the project. As a general rule-of-thumb, the ISA is urged to spend at least one-quarter of the total project time on this 'appreciation' phase. In order to illustrate how this phase can be operationalized a full example is given in Chapter 6 which shows how all members of a medium-sized department were involved in Phase I without undue disruption to the normal operation activities of that department.

The important task to which all involved in Phase I should be dedicated is gaining an appreciation of the problem; that is a tacit agreement between the participants about the nature of the problem situation. This does not mean an *agreement* about the *cause* of the problem but an *acceptance* of a *description* of the problem. The second important task for the client-set is an expression of the component parts of the defined problem. If this phase has an objective as such it would be for the clients to describe the problem in such a way that no member of the enterprise could add to the description in a useful way.

PHASE II

The end of Phase I should become apparent to the participants: they will have expressed the problem situation as well as they can and agreed upon it. Their next task is to move the emphasis away from problem definition towards the description of the information system(s) that seem to underpin the 'systems' involved in the problem itself. The description of the information system can be facilitated by a number of useful modelling methods, some examples of which are discussed in the following chapter. It is the role of the ISA to direct the selection of a variety of modelling methods that seem appropriate to this phase in any one particular situation. It is important that the choice of method should be one that serves the expression of the information system as defined by the clients and should not be selected on the merit of its implications for representing or meeting the technical requirements of the information system.

The model produced should be used (a) as a means of representing the information system(s), (b) as a means of communication among all those involved, and (c) as a means of validating that the information system(s) identified is suited to the needs of the client (e.g. by 'walking' through the model). This is an important area if we are to take the opportunity to consider whether the methods currently in use are the most appropriate methods. Without widening the thinking about possible alternatives at this stage, the result of the analysis would be a translation of current procedures into more efficient procedures. This, of course, presents us with the danger of making any problem inherent in the current procedures more efficient!—a situation not unknown in IT projects.

Phase II of the project development provides an opportunity for the clients to consider information dissemination, storage and 'value'. At this stage the clients should be encouraged to question how the information will be generated and by whom, who will use it and for what purpose, where the information will be stored and what is its value? The need to think about the problem situation as a whole is vital at this point. If changes are to be made to current procedures in order to address perceived problems, then the team need to be certain that making a change in one area will not merely move the 'problem' down the line, or create further unanticipated problems.

PHASE III

This phase is the one that is most familiar to the computer systems analyst. The outcome of Phase III is the production of a technical specification that will support part or all of the information system(s) defined in Phase II. The ISA will call upon his or her technical knowledge to fulfil this part of the project but it is important that the clients are able to relate and comment in a meaningful way upon the specification. It is at this stage that specific technology is advised by the ISA. It is of benefit if the model used in Phase II is one that can be developed into a technical specification (for example, a structured methodology might be appropriate at Phase II and lead into the technical specification of Phase III). It is important to maintain the relationship between Phase II and Phase III through the methods used to represent the information system in order that the clients can continue to exercise control over the design process. However, it is not merely compatibility of methods and models that make this move from Phase I to Phase II possible, but the continued central role of the clients. The active involvement of the clients at this phase will help to assure them that their requirements are not being modified without their full knowledge and approval by technological necessity. Where incompatibility between client requirements and technology exist it should be easily recognized by the clients and dealt with by them, with the ISA, among others, acting as expert consultant.

The clients should be urged to consider questions about the relationship of the technology to the information system specified in Phase II in terms of what the technology will achieve and, perhaps equally importantly, what the technology will not achieve; the effect the technology will have upon the working practices and the training that will be required for all affected by the technology—not only those who will be using the technology but also those who may be affected by its output.

PHASE IV

This is the implementation stage and, if the design process has been undertaken correctly, should be dominated by the clients. The programme for the installation and operation of the IT-supported information system should be determined by the clients, as should the training activities for staff. Clearly, the ISA will provide expert advice to aid the clients in the formulation of the implementation programme but the actions and resources required to support the programme and details relating to how the IT-supported information system is to be made operational is the responsibility of the clients. There are many ways in which the clients can effect this role which, to some degree, will be determined by the particular installation. An example illustrating how one particular group of clients controlled the implementation process is described in Chapters 6 and 7. The clients should be concerned with the effects that the operation of the IT-supported information system might have upon the operation of the enterprise and upon the working practices of the staff at the time of changeover. Contingency plans in the event of failure should be formulated and discussed with the staff involved before the changeover takes place.

PHASE V

Following implementation the clients should gather together a group of 'experts' (i.e. those who work within the enterprise as well as IT-experts) to evaluate the operation of the IT supported information system. Rather than function as an 'inquiry', the meetings should be seen as positive contributions to the on-going process of improving the way that the enterprise operates through the employment of IT and, as such, ideally should be linked to the organization's strategic plans since the installation of IT should not be viewed as the result of a set of actions taken every few years but as part of an on-going process of improvement. It is worth remembering that IT support affects only a part of the information system and the clients' need to continue to review the situation using this process of design is one means of enabling the enterprise to cope with environmental change.

IMPLICATIONS OF CLIENT-LED DESIGN

The argument put forward here is that the successful understanding and definition of an information system may be constrained and misdirected by the practice of placing the technological development of the information system at the centre of the analysis and design process. Instead, it is suggested that what is needed is an holistic approach to the process of information systems design which places at its centre an understanding of the *information system*. At this level of appreciation (the development of which we have discussed under Phase I), there is no need to concern oneself with the technical aspects of the definition. The understanding which is gained through acquiring an appreciation of organizational culture, the information required, how it is used, who it is used by, the form in which it is used, how is it processed, and who shares it will make a fundamental contribution to the satisfactory design and introduction of appropriate technologies. The answers to these questions need to be appreciated not from the ISA's perspective alone but from the perspective of those within the organization.

In order to ensure that this wide understanding is achieved, the composition of the information systems design team needs to be carefully planned if the organization is to take advantage of the experiences of its employees and the opportunities that may be available. The group needs to include members from management and staff who have the credentials to guide the development process (by credentials we mean knowledge of the situation rather than formal qualifications). The technical specification of hardware and software should begin only after Phases I and II have been satisfactory undertaken.

It is likely that the opportunity provided for staff to express opinions will, at first, produce a myriad of views, and many of these views may conflict. This may seem to complicate the information systems design process beyond what is required since what we are ultimately seeking is some formalized, clearly defined way of working. However, it is this process of unravelling the situation and opinions and procedures that is the key to the whole information systems design activity. In many information systems design methodologies, the amount of time spent, first, in defining the problem and, second, in identifying the information system is small compared to the time spent on the technical specification. But since the production of the technical specification can only progress from an initial understanding of the situation, to ignore this fact seems to be short-sighted. However, the increasing use of sophisticated application generator tools, computer-assisted methods of information systems design—including the overall pressure upon consultants and information systems design teams to show results quickly—encourages a lack of attention to the activities in Phase I as well as undue reliance upon the (often) technical-oriented models used at the heart of these tools.

The emphasis being placed here on (a) the early stages of appreciating the situation under investigation, (b) the complete involvement of those working in the situation and (c) the role of the practitioner as a 'facilitator' of this process of learning and appreciation, suggests a different set of activities in the process of information systems development. These new activities, or rather new emphases, and their relationship to each other are illustrated in Figure 2.5.

THE ISA AS 'FACILITATOR'

The modern ISA's role as 'enabler' and 'facilitator' means that he or she should be considered as a member of the information systems design team who has skills in bringing about client-led design which includes both CLD tools and techniques as well as a knowledge of IT. The influence of the ISA, then, should be no greater than any another member of the team who may, for example, have a knowledge of accountancy, production control, or project management. There will be a time in the development process when one member's expertise will be more important than the others, and each member's role in the group should reflect this fact. By adopting this approach the tendency for the IT specialist to predominate in the development process is reduced. If the development process is conducted in this way, then the possibility for real change increases since the recognition and subsequent acceptance (or rejection) of change will come from the group rather than being imposed from outside (Stowell, 1990).

Client-led design is not to be considered as a move to de-skill the role of the ISA; although prestige, authority and status may be seen as being reduced in the areas of technical expertise, other skills on the analytical and management side will be enhanced. Indeed, the skills required for CLD can be argued to be greater and far wider

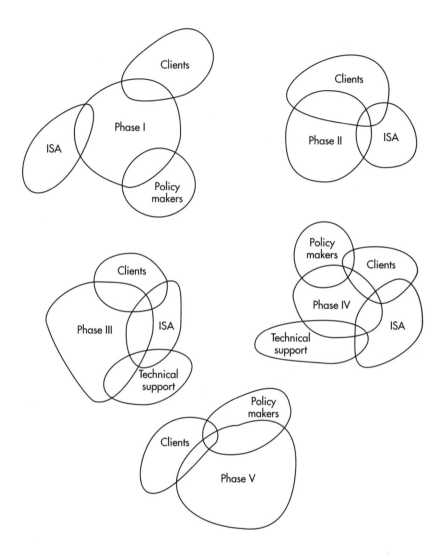

Figure 2.5   Examples of possible interest groups at each phase of CLD

than those for the more traditional methods of computer systems analysis. It is emphasized that the ISA's *technical* expertise is brought into play only in Phase III of the study to indicate to the client where IT may be usefully employed in the informa- tion system that has been specified by the clients. This is not to say, however, that knowledge of technology in terms of its strengths and weaknesses may not be used by the ISA in order to widen the study and its implications. The prime task of the ISA can, therefore, be described as one that produces a description of the necessary information system(s) which is/are likely to include the use of IT rather than one that provides solely an IT solution.

In providing this description we show agreement with Winograd and Flores (1986, p. 6) in that the ISA needs to adopt a view of information systems into which a *variety of technologies* may fit rather than the traditional view of computing systems in which the computer is viewed as the information system. The difficulty facing the ISA is a practical one, namely, that technology requires a *functional* explanation but information involves *understanding*. Despite continuing advances in technology the human is the essential element in an information system since it is the human who can assign meaning to the data processed by the IT. The technology-supported information system, then, can be seen as a mixture of technical and social events causally explained by an observer through a perception of actions during the analysis in which the ISA attempts to unpack and then repack 'reality' into an acceptable design. The shallower the ISA's and the clients' appreciation of the situation then the shallower the analysis and resulting design and, therefore, the likelihood of the technological components failing to fulfil their potential or expectations is increased.

THE CONTRIBUTION OF SYSTEMS THINKING TO CLIENT-LED DESIGN

In order to understand the full requirements of an information system the analyst should not be constrained in his or her investigations by the analytical method used. The method itself should be 'agnostic' to the problem situation: that is, its application should not be limited to a particular problem situation or 'type' of domain. This means that the approach used should not have the rigidity of a step-by-step technique but should be flexible enough to meet different situations and to support an iterative mode of investigation.

What we need, therefore, is a framework within which to undertake the processes involved in analysing and developing an information system. It is important that this framework does not impose its own structure on the problem situation—the approach used should mould itself to fit the problem form, not vice versa. However, at the same time the framework provided must be robust enough to support the information systems development processes involved. In the previous chapter 'systems thinking' was put forward as an appropriate framework for client–led information systems development and it is now appropriate to consider the benefits and opportunities that this approach offers the ISA.

'SOFT' SYSTEMS THINKING AS A BASIS FOR CLIENT-LED DESIGN

In addition to the concept of 'system' as an intellectual construct that we can use to help us think about complexity, systems thinking provides us with a language with which to talk about complexity and a collection of tools and techniques with which it can be modelled, analysed and described. As described in Chapter 1, systems thinking is underpinned by the notion of wholeness, but to imagine that this notion is the sole concern of systems thinkers is an over-simplification. Systems thinking can be shown as having three main streams of thought, as shown in Figure 2.6.

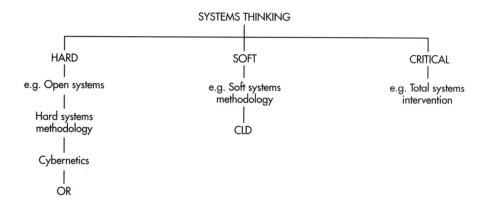

Figure 2.6   Strands of systems thinking

The first stream comprises approaches that have developed from the so-called 'hard' systems view and includes cybernetics, open systems, hard systems method, and operational research. The second stream is categorized as a 'soft' system approach; the best known example is Checkland's soft systems methodology (1981) but it also includes the work of Vickers (1965), Churchman (1968) and Ackoff (1974). The third stream is emerging as some researchers and practitioners explore the contribution of radical social theory as the basis for a critical systems approach (Flood, 1990; Jackson, 1991).

Our intention in this book is not to argue the intellectual origins of these ideas but to exploit ideas and tools, from systems practice as a whole, which we believe are relevant to our purpose in CLD. However, an important contribution to the notion of CLD as described here is the phenomenological and hermeneutic philosophies that underpin the thinking of the so-called 'soft' systems movement, and which, we believe, offer a strong and much needed theoretical basis for information systems.

The difference between 'hard' and 'soft' systems thinking was touched upon in Chapter 1 but is worth reviewing here both as a reminder and so that the description of systems concepts that follows is considered in the appropriate light. We argued that 'hard' systems thinking views the world as a complex web of systems that can be investigated and engineered in order to optimize the system's performance. The language used by 'soft' systems practitioners, on the other hand, reflects their position, which recognizes that systems thinking is solely a way of thinking and learning about reality in order to be able to make decisions about appropriate action: there is no attempt to model and represent reality. Hence soft system models are not a description of what *is* but a representation of what is perceived to be, by some interested party, and modelled using an approach that is considered to be helpful in the discussion of the *notional* system. The word 'notional' is of great importance to stress that the system is named purely for the purpose of investigating the set of activities that this notional system represents and, as such, the naming of a system is intrinsically linked to someone's interest in a particular set of activities. It is this opportunity—represented through soft systems thinking—for organized and clearly structured inquiry into and learning about a problem situation which, it is argued, provides a rich and powerful basis for information systems work (see Figure 2.7).

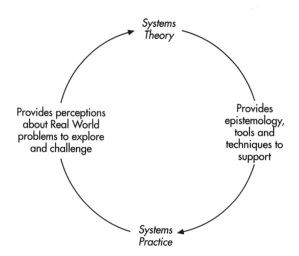

Figure 2.7   Relationship between systems thinking and systems practice

SYSTEMS CONCEPTS

Having outlined the importance of 'wholeness' in systems thinking, and having established the stream of systemic thought from which we are working, in this section we turn our attention to other systems concepts which may be taken up and developed in a way appropriate to CLD as will be illustrated in later chapters.

HOLISM AND CONNECTIVITY

In Chapter 1 we briefly discussed holism as a way of differentiating between systems thinking and reductionist thinking. The aim here is to develop this discussion, giving practical examples. Holism describes a particular way of thinking about the world, in which an attempt is made to look at the whole of a situation rather than just focus on part of a situation. The nature of holistic thinking can be illustrated by comparing it to reductionism. Reductionist thinking, simply stated, is a method of separating the parts of a problem to its smallest and most manageable components. In this way a detailed understanding of the problem is claimed to be possible. The reductionist approach has been demonstrably successful throughout the twentieth century (especially in its guise as 'science'), but when this concept is applied to social situations it can be argued to be less successful. Social situations include a multitude of various elements which, together, make up a social environment. Therefore, as we recognize that there are a variety of interrelationships between the perceived problem situation and other issues from the wider environment within which that problem exists, the relevance of holistic thinking to the study of social situations becomes clearer.

A simple illustration of a reductionist versus holistic approach can be found in the development of the aircraft, Concorde, which has been claimed as a superb feat of engineering; but when it is taken in the wider context, some critics consider it to be an environmental failure. By reducing the goal to that of the technical problem of supersonic passenger transportation, the wider issues of damage to the environment appear to have received less attention than many would have wished. A holistic approach encourages the context of the problem situation to be considered and places emphasis upon understanding how the parts of any notional system are interrelated and the outputs appraised. A notional system in this case could be the production of supersonic and environmentally friendly passenger transportation. Of course further contextual elements may be identified as a wider appreciation of the problem emerges (e.g. political, economical and cultural collaboration).

The diagrams used to illustrate the difference between a purely engineering perspective and a view which takes the wider issues of Concorde development into account (Figure 2.8(a) and (b)) are called systems maps and are a useful way of aiding the thinking about the context of a problem. A more detailed discussion about the use of such diagrams can be found in Chapter 3. Notwithstanding the usefulness of these diagrams in showing the whole problem, they do not indicate how the elements interconnect. Connectivity (Figure 2.9) is a fundamental notion in systems thinking, the idea of which can be formalized to help in two main ways: to help identify relationships and dependencies of notional systems, and to provide a way of checking that the set of activities under investigation can be identified as a system. Failure to identify connectivity is a strong indication that (a) the named activities do not belong in the notional system, or (b) the naming of the system is inaccurate, or (c) important activities in the notional system are not yet defined. It should be remembered that

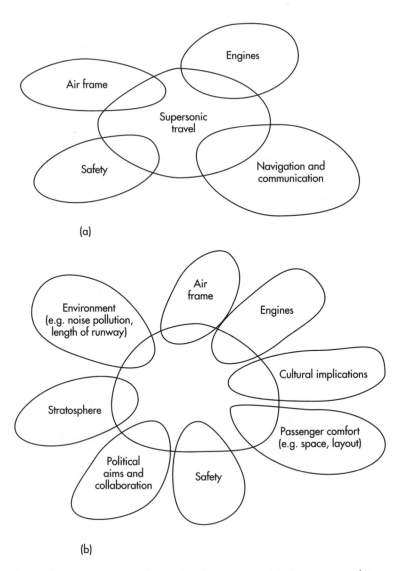

(a)

(b)

Figure 2.8   Systems maps to illustrate reductionist and holistic views of Concorde
development

connectivity may be tangible (e.g. railway network, communication system) or
intangible (e.g. human relationships) or a mixture of both (e.g. gravity).

THE NOTIONS OF SYSTEM, SUBSYSTEM, BOUNDARY AND ENVIRONMENT

By defining a set of activities we are also implicitly using the notion of boundary. The
act of identifying a set of connected activities as being worthy of investigation/
attention means that we are selecting these activities from our appreciation of a vast

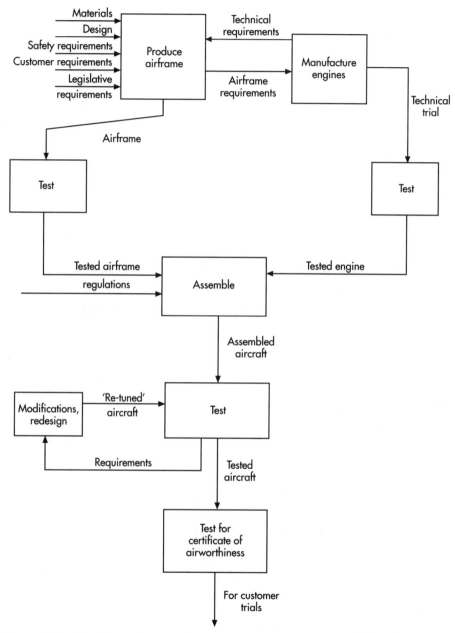

Figure 2.9   Black box diagram showing connectivity in an aircraft development

amount of activities that we judge to be relevant to a problem situation. However, unless we explicitly identify and justify this boundary we are in danger of overlooking or neglecting a rigorous and clear description of our area of interest. The notion of boundary and what exists outside it (its environment) enables the ISA to formalize the boundaries of interest of the project. In practice, a particular boundary may be adopted within the context of time and the design team's growing appreciation of the situation. This is to say that the identification of a boundary is not a once-and-for-all fixed binding of the problem situation but a means of exercising control over the extent of the problem investigation at any one time. A question commonly asked is: 'How does one choose where to place the boundary in a study?' The answer is simple, although for those using the concept incorrectly (e.g. to limit the study and impose a neat but artificial, and probably incorrect, cut-off point) it may seem evasive. The identification of a boundary is dependent upon the individual's understanding of the problem situation and can be used as a means of limiting, controlling and focusing the analytical process at any one time. If it is subsequently decided (as a result of the investigation) that the boundary has been misdrawn, then it should be redefined and the investigation tailored accordingly. This elasticity of boundary-drawing serves to emphasize the importance of the iterative nature of the approach advocated. The 'fixing' of the boundary should only take place when those involved agree the constraints that the boundary will impose upon the study. Much of the discussion in Phase I will help the group to decide the limits of the project's boundary (see Figure 2.10).

The environment of a notional system includes those elements that exert influence on the system of interest but are not directly influenced by that system. Clearly those systems that neither form part of the system in question nor can be justifiably placed in the environment are of no concern for the study of that particular notional system of interest. Obviously the perspective of the individual or group who name the system will direct its form, and, hence, its environment.

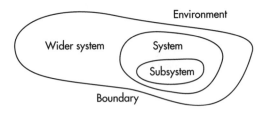

Figure 2.10 Systems map to illustrate the notions of environment, wider system, system, subsystem and boundary

A simple guideline for drawing boundaries is: *Those activities that directly affect the system of interest but are not directly affected by the output of the system should be placed within the system's environment; activities which contribute or are directly affected by the system's output should be placed within the boundary.*

SYSTEM DESCRIPTION

If we wish to consider that a system exists, e.g. an information system, we need to ensure that we can describe it in a way that will aid others to recognize it as a system. To
help in the communication of the ideas that an individual might have about a system
we can, borrowing from Checkland (1981), think of a system in terms of emergence,
hierarchy, communication and control. In describing some notional system we will
also have a 'perspective' from which we recognize and name this system.

HIERARCHY

If we think about the notion of a system existing within a wider system, and a system
being composed of parts which are systems in their own right, then the notion of
hierarchy soon becomes evident. A hierarchy can perhaps best be described diagramat-
ically, as shown in Figure 2.11.

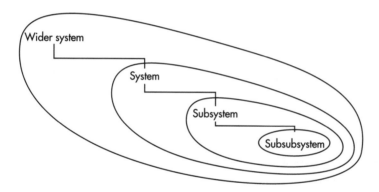

Figure 2.11   Systems map to illustrate a hierarchy of systems

The importance of this notion is to recognize that each part of the notional system is
itself a system, and if we change 'our' system we will affect the subsystems and vice
versa. Moreover, the notional system itself has a relationship to a wider system and to
other systems. For example, the political changes that have taken place in the former
USSR have had significant impact upon the whole political world, and, at a totally
different level, an important man's haircut can disrupt aircraft and create news media
excitement throughout the world.

COMMUNICATION

Communication is the factor that binds a system together and is, therefore, of particular relevance to information systems practitioners. Communication can be described
as the transmission of data from a message originator to some receiver (Figure 2.12).

The originator and receiver are able to attribute meaning to this data which can then be interpreted as information. It is the nature and variety of the ways in which this information is communicated that is of importance to the ISA. The function of any system is highly dependent upon the effectiveness of its communication systems whether the system in question is a living organism or a system designed by people.

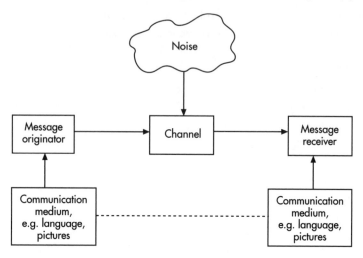

Figure 2.12   A communication system

CONTROL

Control can be described as the mechanism by which a notional system maintains its direction and purpose. Control is effected by the communication of information which acts as a stimuli to the implementation of some corrective action, or 'control'. Therefore, to achieve control we need to know something about the connections between the means of influence and the system's behaviour. If we want to control a system we can operate on its control inputs and, provided we know the connection between the control input values and the output of the system, we can exercise some form of control (Figure 2.13).

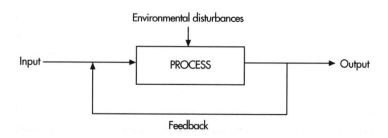

Figure 2.13   Simple control model

A useful and popular example of control in action is the central-heating thermostat without which the central-heating system would degenerate. The thermostat is set to a desired temperature setting which is contrasted to the actual temperature of the space being heated. Any discrepancy between the desired temperature and the actual temperature is monitored and the control mechanism acts to 'correct' this discrepancy (e.g. by increasing the actual temperature by switching on the heating or by decreasing the actual temperature by switching off the heating). Similarly, in a business enterprise there are various control mechanisms to ensure that business goals and objectives are attained (e.g. quality control activities and audits). Without some control mechanism a system will be unable to adjust to changing circumstances and can be expected, eventually, to destroy itself either through uncontrolled growth or decay of the system's output.

Individual perspective from which a 'notional' system is named

It is fairly obvious by now that many of the systems we have described are systems because that is the way that we, as individuals, see them. While there will be agreement about many aspects of certain systems (e.g. human reproduction, the London Underground), others will be more contentious (e.g. terrorism, health care). One way to overcome this problem is to exert enough power to squash all opposing views, but evidence suggests that the latter course of action is unsuccessful in the longer term. An alternative might be to recognize other views and try to get others involved in the problem situation to do the same. This does not mean, of course, that this will lead to a general agreement but it may help in the information system development process.

In any situation the individuals and groups involved may not see the situation in exactly the same way. Different social background, upbringing, lifestyle, personal experience, beliefs, values and norms all play their part in forming a judgement about the world. Consequently, individuals and groups bring their own perspectives, or viewpoints, to bear when attributing meaning to any activity. Even where it is possible to identify events in which many may share a similar viewpoint (e.g. a political opinion), there may be different shades of that particular view when these issues are discussed in detail. (Systems thinking itself provides a good example of the richness of divergences within a generally accepted category.) Our individual viewpoint will affect our 'readiness' to appreciate a situation from a different angle, and may also direct our view of the context of the problem (Vickers, 1965). For example, the advocates of nuclear power, who see the potential of this source of energy for the future, may find an environmentalist's argument about pollution difficult to appreciate within the context of an energy crisis and the world economy. An environmentalist, on the other hand, may find the safety, ethical and moral issues involved impossible to ignore in spite of the growing cost of other forms of energy. Two possible descriptions of the extreme views outlined above could be as follows: (1) concern about the provision of energy in the future and the dependence of the world economy on the availability of energy, and (2) concern about the way in which past experience of the use of nuclear technology has shown that it cannot always be controlled. Developing these views into a notional system to describe the production of nuclear energy would focus attention upon different aspects of the situation which, in turn, if modelled, would produce two quite different sets of activities, both of which would be relevant to a particular viewpoint (Figure 2.14).

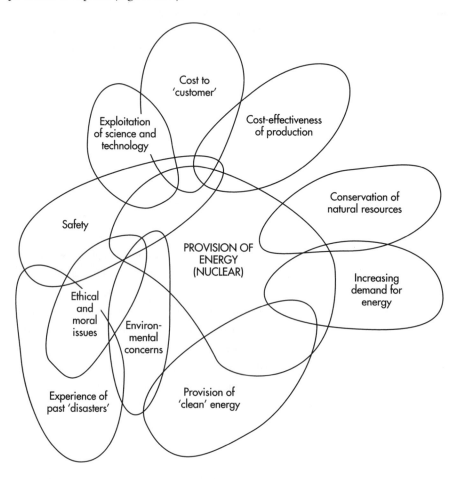

Figure 2.14   Systems map showing different and overlapping perspectives

World view, or Weltanschauung ('W'), as described by Dilthey (1961), related to what might be described as significant personal influences through which an individual makes sense of the world. For Dilthey world views are described through an analysis of the historical developments of religion, poetry and metaphysics (Rickman, 1976).

The position that we take in this text is less proscribed. We are more concerned with the formal recognition that differing views about any given system exist rather than attempt to explain in detail how they might be formed. In an information system development process the individual's view of the problem and the context of the problem will shape the requirements of the system itself. This assertion, of course, will not surprise anyone, but for the ISA this is a difficult aspect and it is vital that these views are explored and taken into account in the design process. Phase I of CLD provides an opportunity to address and manage the multiplicity of views that exist within the project domain.

EMERGENCE AND SYNERGY

An important characteristic of notional systems is their potential to demonstrate what is referred to as a synergistic relationship. A synergistic relationship is one that is judged to have an output of greater value than the sum of the outputs of its individual parts. This is a significant systems concept in that it highlights the importance of adopting a holistic view of any situation, since relying upon an analysis of individual parts is likely to result in an analysis that relates to only a part of the system's output. In this way much of the richness of a situation is easily lost.

An important example of synergy can be found in what Checkland (1981) refers to as an 'emergent property' (the notion of 'organizational culture' discussed above can be seen as an example of an emergent property). An emergent property is the output of a system, recognized by some interested party as being above and beyond the identifiable outputs of the system's subsystems: a kind of by-product which, of course, can both enhance or counteract the aim of the organization. Furthermore, it may be the way in which the components are arranged that support particular emergent properties (e.g. the social and physical layout of an office). Although a particular emergent property may be sought by introducing controls and standards into the system, it may also be generated in a way that is seemingly inexplicable. Examples of emergent properties that are relatively easy to identify can be found in the following organizations: Rolls Royce, Woolworth's, Marks and Spencer, Harrod's, Dorothy Perkins, Oxford University, McDonald's Hamburgers; and in inanimate objects: an impressionist painting, the Pompidou Centre, St. Paul's Cathedral, Chanel No. 5, a Rolex watch, furry dice, a Ferrari. These examples are all fairly obvious although their emergent properties may differ from person to person. For example, one person may view St Paul's Cathedral as an elegant piece of architecture, symbolizing the glory of Britain's past achievements and representing one of the most praiseworthy buildings in the country. Another may view it as an ugly, old-fashioned and useless building which takes up valuable and much needed prime-site real estate. Similarly, Marks and Spencer's may be seen as providing off-the-peg quality garments at an unbeatable price together with a valuable no-quibble, money-back guarantee. Others may see it as providing staid and uninnovative products at a relatively high price and enforcing a peculiar refusal to accommodate customers' growing use of international credit cards, recognizing only their own.

REVIEW QUESTIONS

As a means of reflecting upon the content of this chapter, consider the meaning and significance of the following concepts:

Holism   Control

Boundary   Connectivity

System, subsystem   Communication

Environment   Hierarchy

Synergy and emergent property   Individual perspective

Weltanschauung

EXERCISES:

(1) Explain the notions of 'system', 'wider-system', 'subsystems' and 'environment' by describing an organization known to you in terms of Fig. 2.9 above.

(2) Consider and describe the emergent properties of: Rolls-Royce, Oxford University; Sky television.

(3) Identify the hierarchy of retailing outlets that can be identified in the food retailing system, e.g. supermarket, hypermarket, corner shop.

(4) Identify the different viewpoints that might be considered within the context of developing a new technology-based information system into an organization that has, until now, used little information technology. Consider the boundaries of the views you have identified. Do these boundaries overlap or are they mutually exclusive?

(5) Compare the nature of reductionist and systems thinking as approaches to problem-solving.

(6) Outline the benefits of adopting a systems approach as a framework for implementing a client-led approach to information systems design and development.

3

DESCRIBING AND MODELLING SYSTEMS USING SYSTEMS TOOLS

INTRODUCTION: THE 'APPRECIATIVE' SETTING

In Chapter 1 we described the five phases of client-led design (CLD) and emphasized the importance of iteration between the different phases. In Chapter 2 the central role of Vickers' notion of 'appreciation' in CLD was discussed and argued to be the foundation of an approach to identifying and designing information systems that is developed upon the premise that learning about the situation and the views, needs and expectations of those involved is of fundamental importance. Having established this appreciation of the situation, it was argued (in Phase I) that the analysis and design process might then continue from, what is expected to be, a thorough understanding of the situation under investigation from the points of view of both the ISA and the client-set. It is this joint and mutually supported appreciation of the situation that forms the backbone of CLD. Although, having moved through Phase I, the study can be expected to become more concerned with identifying relevant information systems and exploring the possible contribution of IT to these information systems, the notion of seeking an appreciation and its significance in helping to support a shared understanding should not be forgotten: it should be extended throughout the study as a whole and, as such, strengthens the project and the commitment of the individuals involved to the design and developmental procedures as well as to the final outcomes of the study. Figure 3.1 is offered as a simple diagrammatic representation of this process.

For a more detailed discussion of Vickers' work the reader should refer to the following chapter where it is discussed in relation to organizational models that support CLD. The aim of this chapter, however, is to consider and propose how systems thinking (primarily through diagrams) can offer the ISA a practical set of tools. The emphasis will be placed upon the use of these diagrams in Phase I (appreciation) of the framework for CLD set out in the previous chapter. Before we move on to looking at the tools it seems appropriate at this point to offer a brief discussion of the

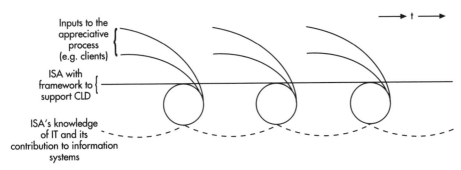

Figure 3.1   Diagrammatic representation of the dynamic process of
              'appreciation' and its contribution to the process of client-led design
              for information system analysis

nature of models and their use in terms of both formal diagrammatic models (of which
type many are developed through the use of the tools presented in this chapter) and
the more complex, conceptual models discussed in the following chapter.

MODELS AND MODELLING

Whenever we describe or express some activity, either through words or diagrams,
what we are doing is creating a model of that activity. This notion of model represents
some abstraction of our perception of the reality and, if careful, we choose our
modelling medium to highlight and emphasize what we take to be the important
aspects of the activity we model. A useful description of the modelling process is
offered by Wilson (1984) who explains that in modelling a situation we are using a
particular set of intellectual constructs through which to view it. Each set of constructs
may be developed into a practical form as some model that can be 'likened to a filter
so that the image of the real world is particular to the characteristics of the filter and is
determined by them' (Wilson, 1984. p. 4). Consequently, one particular activity may
be modelled in a variety of ways, each of which might show the activity in a different
light. To a great extent the success of the modelling exercise rests upon the skill of the
modeller in terms of an ability to:

- understand the activity, or situation, to be modelled;
- understand the nature of different models, together with their implications
  and significances; and
- select and use these models in a meaningful and useful fashion.

Ackoff (1962) offers a distinction between three types of model, namely, iconic,
analogic, and analytic. Wilson (1984) suggests a further type of model which he calls
'conceptual'. An iconic model is a scaled down (or up) version of reality, the proper-

ties of which equate to those of the real article (albeit on a different scale), so that the model can be expected to behave in the same way as the real article (e.g. an automobile model for safety testing). With an analogic model the behaviour of the model is expected to simulate that of the original although the physical appearance of the model is quite different to that of the article being modelled (e.g. a computer program that simulates the flow of stock in a warehouse). An analytic model is one developed from mathematical or logical relationships that are believed to underlie the behaviour of some situation of interest (e.g. mathematical model of accounting). An analytic model may provide the building blocks for an analogic model. Wilson offers a fourth type, a conceptual model, which covers the pictorial/symbolic model that, although a model in its own right, is often developed before any other type of modelling takes place. Typically, such models are used to represent the subjective and qualitative aspects of a situation.

Whichever type of model we choose to adopt we must be certain of its intended use. For example, a model can be used as a kind of 'template' that is used in order to structure some situation. Through this process of forming and structuring much can be learned about the situation in terms of its similarities and deviations from the model. The process of actually using a model as a vehicle for inspecting 'reality' may cause us to reinvestigate 'reality' in areas in which our knowledge is deficient and thus may provide a useful learning mechanism. In this manner a model may be a way of comparing some situation with what has been proved to be an 'ideal' type or an optimal and desirable format. A model may be built in order to test, as realistically as possible—given that the model is only an abstraction of the 'real' thing—potential results in certain situations. In this sense the model may allow us to 'simulate' particular circumstances and assess the results without having to 'experiment' upon 'reality'. Finally, a model may be used to provide us with a means of communicating with others our perceptions and ideas so that they may be discussed openly and jointly. Whatever our use of a model, it is of the utmost importance to remember that a model is, with varying degrees of accuracy, an abstraction of our perception of 'reality': it is neither 'reality' itself nor even an exact replicate of 'reality'. This warning applies as equally to models of 'soft', human activity in which personal views and experience shape our perceptions as it does to models of 'hard', factual situations since it may be argued that it is always possible to find some deviation of the model from 'reality', whether it be on account of possible assumptions that need to be built into the model or on account of being unable to supply absolute measures of 'reality'. A model of a situation, regardless of size or complexity, is the result of one's understanding of a situation and the aspects we choose to model will be the result of what Vickers calls our 'readinesses' (or lack of them) to take note of or recognize aspects of reality as being relevant to our model.

The use of models—diagrams and verbal forms—can play an important role during all phases of CLD but is particularly useful during Phase I as a means of promoting discussion and learning about the problem situation as we shall illustrate in the remainder of this chapter.

DEFINING A NOTIONAL SYSTEM

A major contribution of systems thinking to CLD is the notion of thinking about the problem situation in terms of meaningful 'wholes' or 'systems' (i.e. sets of connected parts viewed by some party as a whole which does something that is recognized to be relevant to the situation under investigation). This approach offers us not only the benefit of being able to break down a complex situation into manageable parts but prevents us from losing sight of the whole, or the context, in which the part exists. Failure to recognize the importance of the whole may result in only viewing parts of the problem situation and may seduce us into recommending 'quick fixes' which may give the impression of solving the problem but, in practice, cause the problem to resurface elsewhere since the underlying deficiency was not addressed. Furthermore, by viewing the situation systemically we are adopting a firm but unrestricting framework for our analysis; it is an approach that can be ordered, explained and investigated rather than being merely a good but commonsense approach.

The problem of defining a notional system that is useful to the study can be difficult and time-consuming but is of utmost importance since our naming of a relevant system will then dictate the way we model that system which, in turn, may direct subsequent investigation. Therefore, having begun by identifying some activity relevant to the problem situation, the next step is to develop this into a full system description. A useful starting point is to begin: 'A system to...' and then continue by stating the central purpose of this activity (e.g. to provide information; to monitor the assignment of....; to sample...). At the heart of this description will be some verb (or collection of dependent verbs). Having arrived at the description of a relevant system, it is then important to ensure that what we have identified can, indeed, be described as a *system*. Any purposeful system has at its core some form of process whereby inputs are processed into outputs (Figure 3.2). It is useful to think of this processing as a *transformation* and to make explicit the process that brings about this transformation. One way of doing this is to consider the input and output of the system and to describe how one has been transformed into the other.

When we describe the transformation affected by a named system then implicit in this description is the view of the namer of the system, which makes the transformation of the system meaningful. This was referred to above as the 'individual perspective'—the world view or perspective that justifies and explains the transformation. It is useful to

Figure 3.2   The transformation process of a system

state this perspective explicitly so that the transformation represented by the system can be regarded in the light of the appropriate perspective. It may be that different perspectives about a given process yield substantially different transformations, although the change in emphasis stated through the individual perspective may be quite subtle.

Other important elements can also be named, either implicitly or explicitly, from the transformation named in the system description. The investigation of the named system will benefit from answering the following questions:

(1) Given the named transformation, who are those people or groups who are work-ing to achieve the transformation?
(2) What aspects are likely to constrain or limit the success of the transformation?
(3) Who is ultimately responsible for seeing that the transformation process is achieved?
(4) Who are the people or groups who will be most affected by the result of the transformation?

All these elements can be expected to play an important role in effecting the named transformation, and they merit careful consideration in an effort to understand the notional system. Figure 3.3 illustrates the significance of these elements to the named transformation.

EXPLORING THE ISA'S INVOLVEMENT: A STATEMENT OF AWARENESS

In working towards identifying the transformation and perspective within any given system, it may be useful to try to structure our thinking about the problem situation and our own position within it. To help us achieve this there are certain things we can think about. For example, how much do we actually understand about the situation and what is our personal interest? When we encounter a problem we must recognize that we are approaching it from a particular angle and/or for a particular reason. If a bridge falls down then we could be examining this problem on behalf of the construction company that assembled it or on behalf of those investigating the accident: two groups interested for different reasons, united by the accident itself.

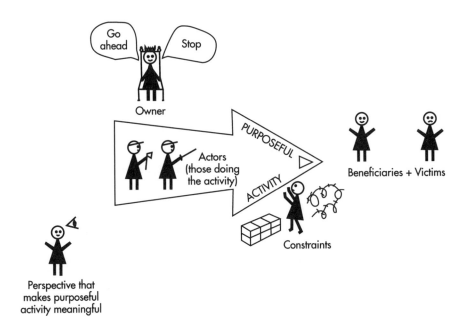

Figure 3.3   Describing purposeful activity encapsulated in a description of a notional system (after Checkland and Scholes, 1990)

Similarly, when we are looking at an information system within a company, we must be aware of our perspective. We could be looking at it on behalf of a consultancy which also markets a particular software package, or we could be part of the company management team acting on a policy from the directorate to streamline the company staffing levels through the application of IT. Whichever role the ISA is playing, it may seriously affect/influence the study and the way it is undertaken.

One useful way of ensuring that we are aware of the situation is to make our role and interest explicit. We can work towards this by considering certain elements: we make our perspective of the transformation named in the system explicit by identifying our 'perspective' but we can develop this further by describing our 'state' at the beginning of the analysis process and by explaining why we are interested in studying this set of activities and the motives behind our interest. It is not necessary that others are privy to such descriptions, but it is important that we have these things clear in our minds at the beginning of the project. Alternatively, such statements of interest and intent may be used as a method of establishing a clear understanding and agreement with the client about what is required of the investigation and those playing active roles. Where teams of people are involved (as will be the case with CLD projects) it may be necessary for each member of the group to state his or her interest and intent and these statements could, with agreement, be used to help develop an understanding of the context of the problem situation.

USING DIAGRAMS TO MODEL NOTIONAL SYSTEMS

In order to explore the possible form (structure and function) of named systems it is important to be able to represent the system in some way. By naming a system, a boundary is implicitly declared for the system that you have decided is of interest (in conjunction with your clients). Naming a system is an important and often quite difficult process since the inclusion of one word may alter the sense and, therefore, the description or definition of the system of interest. For example, a system to *support the provision* of information to a particular individual is a very different system to the one that *provides* the required information. The system's name should be carefully developed to encapsulate the nature of the system—a process that may take some time and which may benefit from discussion with as many of those involved as possible.

Having identified a system that we feel would benefit exploration we can then begin to think about modelling it in order to help describe its structure and processes and, if appropriate, to help predict the behaviour of that system. We can adopt many different system modelling tools and techniques but whichever we use it is useful to consider the following points (or at least use them as a mental checklist) in order to enhance one's application of the selected tools and techniques and to increase one's awareness of the situation:

- Is the transformation of identified inputs into identified outputs clearly stated?
- Is some viewpoint or perspective, from which the transformation is seen to be justifiable, expressed?
- What subsystems of the notional system enable and affect the transformation process?
- Are the boundary and environment clearly known?
- What monitoring and controlling activities are present?
- Is there connectivity and communication between activities in the system and subsystem?

SYSTEMS DIAGRAMS AND MODELS FOR PHASE I

Before moving on to look at diagrams and models for particular use during the appreciation phase of CLD (Phase I), it is worth while reminding the reader that CLD is a philosophical framework for structuring and managing the process during which clients play a major role in designing their own computer-based information systems to suit their information needs. Consequently, what follows in this chapter is a collection, or 'tool-box', of techniques that the ISA might call upon which support the process of appreciation particularly well. It is not an attempt to provide a unified and regimented method of CLD. While the diagrams and models that follow may be used as stand-alone techniques, they may also be used in conjunction with one another to build up a more detailed picture of the problem situation. Table 3.1 summarizes the stages at which, and the methods in which, the different techniques may be most usefully employed.

Table 3.1   A example of when and how the diagrammatic techniques discussed in this chapter may be employed

Systems tools	Attribute	CLD
Transformation	What the system is meant to do	Phase I
Spray diagrams	Show the logical relationship between elements of a problem	Phase I
Decision tree	Weighting of risks associated with decisions	Phase I/II
The systems map	Visual representation of problem situation, its parts and interrelationships	Phase I/II
Control models	Representation of a system showing the essential control elements	Phase I/II/V
Causal loop and influence diagrams	A means of representing views and The 'behaviour' of the system	Phase I/II/V
Black box diagrams	Representation system and the relationship between its parts	Phase I/II/V
Rich pictures	Means of representing 'hard' and 'soft' elements of a situation	Phase I
Activity models	Diagrammatic representation of activities that need to take place in a notional system	Phase I
Structured methods and object-oriented analysis	Methods of depicting a client's perceived information system which can easily be developed into a technical specification	Phase II/III

In order to explore a notional system it is useful to be able to represent the system diagrammatically. The rigour involved in producing a good systems diagram has four major benefits: it crystallizes thinking; it aids communication with others; it provides documentation; and it enables 'walkthroughs' to be undertaken (to 'test' the behaviour of the named system by working through a particular problem). For this purpose we may adopt a number of systems diagrams: systems maps (venn diagram convention); spray diagrams; influence/causal loop diagrams; black box diagrams; conceptual/activity models; rich pictures; structured data flow diagrams; OOA models. In the remainder of this chapter these different techniques and diagrams are discussed and illustrated. We have tried to ensure that standard conventions (where they exist) are adhered to. Obviously, it is important to try to maintain the convention of any diagram used since the diagram format has been developed to support the representation of information in a particular way. While failure to conform to the diagram convention means that the diagram may not represent the situation as expected, and thereby fail to fulfil the diagram's potential, we also recognize that diagram conventions may need to be structured to fit the situation. Indeed, it is often these evolving representations that can be the most useful, although we advise that the conventions of any 'new' or 'hybrid' diagram are carefully described to avoid confusion.

SPRAY DIAGRAMS

The spray diagram (or spider diagram) is a useful way of recording facts at the time of interview or data collection and provides a means of ordering these facts into clusters of related points. The construction of the diagram begins from a centre point of logic from which various branches of thought can be recorded and developed. For example, if the client is discussing marketing requirements there may be one main branch that relates to the activities of the marketing section, another that relates to after-sales service, another that relates to finance and accounts, another to research and development, and so on (Figure 3.4). Each of the branches may have any useful number of smaller branches upon which the more detailed facts relating to each branch is recorded; these branches themselves may divide into 'twigs' to capture finer detail or related ideas. It is possible that some elements may belong to several separate branches, in which case it is up to the author of the diagram to decide how this can best be recorded—should the recurring element be included on both branches or should the branches be linked? The decision should be based upon the purpose of the diagram and the effect either approach might have on the overall appearance and clarity of the diagram.

DECISION TREE

A decision tree is similar in many respects to a spray diagram except we add probabilities to help weight the possible decisions and hence provide an aid for the decision

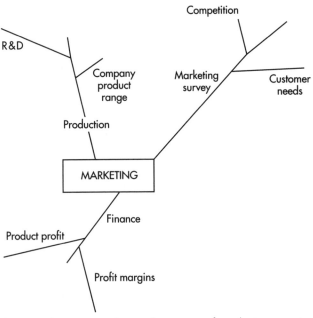

Figure 3.4   A spray diagram exploring the notion of marketing requirements

maker (Figure 3.5). The advantage of a decision tree is that it is a simple display of various routes to decisions which the decision taker can quickly assimilate. A simple explanation of decision analysis is that we need to consider the chances of a decision being correct. For example, consider what the chance of being correct would there be if we predicted that night follows day. We have almost 100 per cent chance of being correct, or, as a probability on a scale of 0–1, we allocate a probability of 1. When considering other situations, such as predicting which horse will win a horse race, we are less sure, e.g. 10 per cent chance of being correct, or 0.1 probability. Clearly we can make a prediction about each of the branches of the decision tree. The more accurate our assessment, the more accurate the decision model itself. However, we have discussed the limitations of models earlier in this chapter, so remember that the decision tree is no more than an aid to decision-making; it will not provide a guaranteed correct answer.

In Figure 3.5 we are attempting to assess the chance of correctly predicting the outcome of the success of a new product called 'Zuffrane'. In the first case we predict that the chance of the product selling well within the first six months with good advertising is about 30 per cent (0.3 probability), and if for the next six months we do not advertise then there is a 50 per cent chance if the salesforce do their jobs well or a maybe a 0.5 probability if we allow the sales representatives do their own advertising. The second branch says that if after three months we advertise on a small scale then

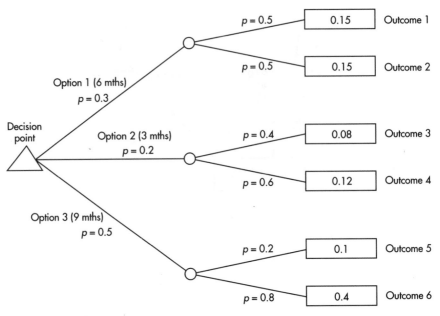

Figure 3.5   A decision tree

we expect our chances to be about 20 per cent and up to 60 per cent by the year end if we spend more on advertising and 40 per cent if we continue at the same rate. In the third option we decide to advertise on a national scale and for the first nine months expect a 0.5 probability of success, leaving us with a decision not to advertise any further, which we think will give us a 0.2 probability of success, or to continue with the national advertising which, in the last three months, we feel will improve our chances of selling the product by 80 per cent. The outcome in each case is what we predict will be the overall probability of being correct, e.g. in the first option the probability is $0.3 \times 0.5 = 0.15$, and outcome 6 giving us a 0.4 chance of success, which seems to be the best option. To make the decisions more realistic we could add estimates of costs for each advertising strategy, which would help us with our decision-making.

THE SYSTEMS MAP

The purpose of a systems map is to enable the practitioner to represent major elements of the named system and their relationship to each other. The systems map is often one of the first diagrams used once the notional system has been defined using the ideas of system boundary and environment as described in the previous chapter. Two forms of the systems map may be usefully employed which use these systems elements in slightly different ways. An example of the first type of systems map is shown in Figure 3.6.

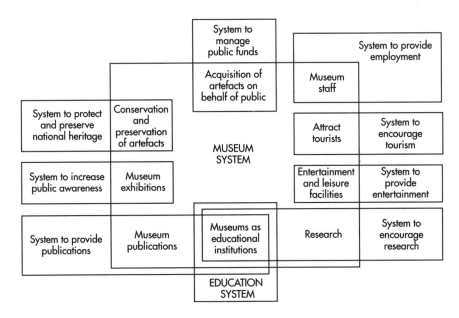

Figure 3.6 Systems map of a 'museum' system

With the second type of systems map the system of interest still provides the name or description of the central whole but, this time, elements relevant to this system are placed within the system boundary. Relevant environmental factors are placed outside the systems boundary, as shown in Figure 3.7.

CONTROL MODELS

In the previous chapter we introduced the notion of 'control' and discussed its importance to systems thinking. In this section we focus upon the practical application of this concept and the models which illustrate or embody control principles.

Open loop control

We can develop quite complicated control systems by setting out a list of rules. For example, consider advising someone how to use a cash dispenser at a bank. The following is a list of activities which an individual might undertake in order to get cash from the dispenser:

(1) Insert card into slot
(2) Key in personal number
(3) Select appropriate menu at the prompt
(4) Input desired transaction
(5) Terminate transaction programme

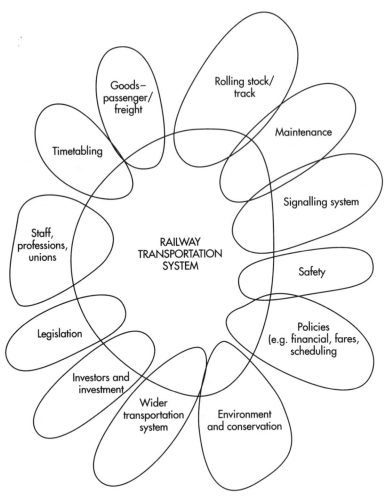

Figure 3.7 Systems map of railway transportation system

(6) Remove card

(7) etc.

This kind of control is called *open loop control.* The control system is fairly limited because it depends heavily upon the actual inputs to the observed system remaining constant (within a relatively narrow band of alternatives) and upon the control input setting and output value. While open loop control can help to achieve a goal it is not possible to make corrections if the output drifts off course. For example, if the person puts the bank card in the wrong way or fails to react correctly to the prompt, the dispenser cannot compensate for the error but must default back to some error message or set behaviour, such as the return of the card, and the user must begin the cycle again. A familiar method of open loop control, which will be known to computer scientists, is the decision tables (Figure 3.8). Decision tables can be used for a number of purposes, but however they are used the construction of the tables will place constraints upon the possible outputs.

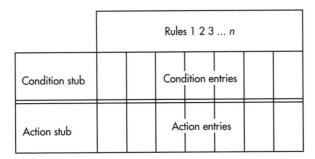

Figure 3.8   Decision table

A limited entry table requires a 'Y' (true) or 'N' (false) to be entered in the condition entry column, and, in the action entry column, an 'X' if action is to be taken or a '—' if entry is not to be taken. The rule column defines the actions that follow on from the defined outcomes. A simple example of a limited entry decision tree might be one in which a customer's credit status is checked, as shown in Figure 3.9.

	1	2	3	4
Is the order within customer limits?	Y	Y	N	N
Has the customer cleared costs?	Y	N	Y	N
Raise order	X	X	–	–
Refer to manager	–	–	X	–
Refer to customer	–	–	–	X

Figure 3.9   Limited entry decision table

The previous example is a trivial one but it serves to illustrate both open loop control and the relationship of this idea to one of the tools commonly used by CSAs. For a more detailed discussion of decision tables, see Parkin (1987).

Feedback – closed loop control

The idea of feedback control is not new since its origins can be traced back to the third century BC (Mayr, 1969). It was the recognition that the principles of feedback control systems, which can be seen in engineering mechanisms (e.g. thermostats), could be applied to other systemic activity that led to the exploitation of these ideas in other areas of human endeavour (e.g. production control; quality control; management).

Feedback control is characterized by its closed loop structure and can be defined as one 'which tends to maintain a prescribed relationship of one system variable to another by comparing functions of these variables and using the difference as a means of control' (AIIE Committee Report, 1951). In exercising feedback control what we are attempting to do is to reduce the effect of change to a system (e.g. due to changes in desired output, environmental disturbances and inconsistent inputs and system processing behaviour) through exerting control by compensating, where necessary, for the difference between the actual and the required output of the system. This type of control is called *closed loop control* since we are closing the loop between output and input. As can be seen in Figure 3.10, samples of the actual output may be taken and compared with the desired output so that suitable decisions can be made about a strategy for future action that helps to compensate for the deviation detected.

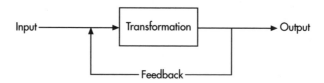

Figure 3.10   Simplified diagram of feedback control

It is not always easy to exercise control since it may take time for the effects of the changes to the input (the result of the 'correction' strategy) to reach the output. The time delay between the moment of operating the control and the effect appearing in the output is called *lag*. Lag is a common term used in engineering and can be either counteracted or used to benefit when considering the design of information systems. For example, it may be necessary to ensure that the lag in a closed loop control system does not result in the controller overcontrolling the system because earlier control actions have not had time to filter through and be picked up at the output sample point (e.g. stock control systems). In other cases lag may be a useful way of slowing down and making the control of a system more manageable and, hence, more stable (e.g. the Stock Exchange).

Positive and negative feedback.
The type of feedback used in a closed loop control system can be of two kinds: positive or negative.

Positive feedback: As the output of a system moves in any direction (increases or decreases), the feedback message acts on the input in such a way as to cause the output to move in the same direction even further. For example, think about the effect of a computer-based information system in a stock market (e.g. London or New York). If, as happened at the time of the Stock Exchange Crash in 1989, computer programs designed to detect patterns in the sale of shares, detect such a pattern and trigger off a share-selling program, this reaction then becomes part of the overall selling pattern, which in turn triggers off more selling, and the cycle is repeated until it self-destructs. From this example, it can be seen that the nature of positive feedback is that it will finally destroy the system, unless interrupted by either perpetual growth or perpetual decay (Figure 3.11). This is not to say that positive feedback should be avoided at all costs: it may be used to great effect if there is some need to promote growth (e.g. to start a business enterprise) or to encourage decay (e.g. an economic and environmental need to reduce the birth rate).

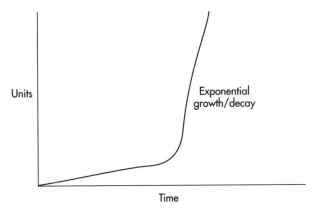

Figure 3.11   The 'shape' of positive feedback

Negative feedback: As the output of a system moves away from the desired output, then control action is induced and the output is pulled back towards the desired output. Owing to the lag in the control system, the output is likely to continue its movement past the desired state. A further comparison of the output with the desired output induces further control action and the output is pulled back towards the desired state. The overall behaviour of such control is oscillation towards the desired state until equilibrium is maintained (Figure 3.12). This, therefore, produces a stable and controlled system.

For this reason negative rather than positive feedback is used to control systems since it acts to reduce errors and enables the 'goal' of the system to be achieved. A good example of the practical effect of negative feedback in a business enterprise is the control exercised over the business as a whole by the finance department. The installa-tion of computing power to process the company accounts and provide up-to-date trading details enables the management of the enterprise to ensure that the company is achieving its targets. A fall in sales (and hence income) can be examined and a strategy to improve performance can then be initiated. Conversely, an unplanned increase in sales which exceeds production capacity can be brought under control quickly.

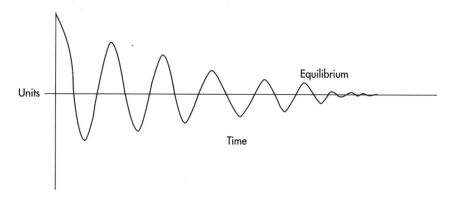

Figure 3.12   The 'shape' of negative feedback

The benefits of using IT to monitor and control a system can be well illustrated by this same business example. Use of IT has enabled managers to collect and analyse relevant data about the organization and its performance far more quickly and in more detail than was possible when using manual methods. The speed at which computers can process data allows managers to make better informed and quicker decisions, the result of which is to reduce the lag in the organizational control system and thereby provide the opportunity for a tighter and quicker responding control over organiza-tional activities (e.g. Just-In-Time stock management).

It is the overall behaviour of the 'system' which distinguishes between positive and negative feedback and not its physical appearance. Let us consider a phenomenon that most of us have experienced: the howling effect that occasionally occurs with a public address system. At a particular frequency a 'howl' is audible, indicating that the public address system is unstable at this frequency and, hence, could be said to exhibit positive feedback. This frequency is related to the delay of the sound from the loudspeaker back to the microphone. At other frequencies there is the same amplifica-tion, but because of the delay in the feedback path the signal fed back does not augment the input signal, giving negative feedback. We can therefore identify positive feedback at some frequencies and negative feedback at others, despite the fact that the feedback path has not been altered.

To ignore the effects of feedback can have serious consequences which are evident from the major environmental difficulties that we, the human race, face. Ill-considered use of positive and negative feedback can have far-reaching and undesirable effects, and the effect of feedback can be nowhere greater than in the information system domain. At one level we are concerned with the application of a variety of technological devices to perceived information systems and at another level we are interfering with existing communication systems, or creating new ones. The implementation of technology will alter the way in which a given 'system' operates and the ISA should be mindful of the kind of feedback systems involved in the notional system being considered.

INFLUENCE AND CAUSAL LOOP DIAGRAMS

There is frequently some confusion in the literature concerning the nature of influence diagrams and causal loop diagrams although both are appropriate methods of illustrating and exploring the type of control behaviour that any notional system, subsystem or wider system may exhibit. We find it useful to distinguish between the two types of diagram in the following way:

(1) The notion of 'influence' refers to the relationship whereby one component affects another but does not necessarily 'cause' it to happen—e.g. height influences weight but does not necessarily cause it.
(2) A causal loop diagram is used where evidence suggests a causal process—e.g the excessive consumption of alcohol causes a change in behaviour. The conventions for drawing causal loop diagrams is that the direction of the arrow head indicates causality and the sign (positive or negative) shows the effect of the causality.

These types of diagram have a number of uses. For example, an influence diagram could be used to represent the 'context' of a situation including the relationship between those activities, groups, or individuals involved. The relationships between the various elements can be illustrated by indicating whether the influences are positive or negative (as in positive or negative feedback). This notion is illustrated in Figure 3.13.

A note on positive and negative feedback

It is important to remember the ways in which positive and negative feedbacks work. A general rule of thumb is that when a relationship is promoted in the same direction, the charge is positive: it acts to reinforce the direction of influence (e.g. 'the *less* cars on the road, the *less* pollution from cars' and 'the *more* cars on the road the *more* pollution' are both examples of positive charges). Negative relationships are those which 'correct' the direction (e.g. the '*greater* the price of petrol, the *less* cars on the

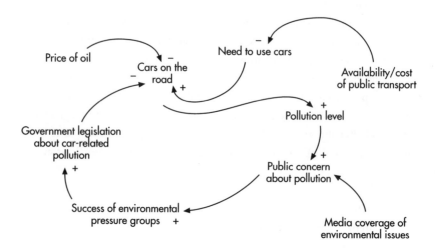

Figure 3.13   Example of an influence diagram including positive and negative
feedback loops

road'). However, the nature of the complete loop offers the most helpful information.
For example, consider:

(1) The *more* cars on the road then the *more* pollution.
(2) The *more* pollution then the *greater* the public concern about pollution levels.
(3) The *greater* the public concern for pollution levels then the *stricter* (greater) the
     government legislation about car usage.
(4) The *stricter* (greater) the legislation about car usage then the *less* cars on the road.

Of course, on the second time round the loop the action will be continued in the
direction of 'less' which will still be positive until we get to 'the *less* strict the legislation, the *greater* the number of cars on the road', where we find the negative relationship that acts to control the whole system (i.e. the whole activity is therefore a
negative feedback system).

Advice on drawing influence/causal loop diagrams
When drawing an influence or causal loop diagram it is useful to begin by trying to
identify a number of activities that are relevant to the domain and then consider the
influential relationships. Once a skeleton frame is provided for the system of interest
(Figure 3.14), then further relevant activities can be identified and added to the
diagram (Figure 3.15).

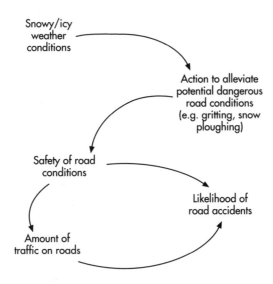

Figure 3.14   Development of the causal loop diagram

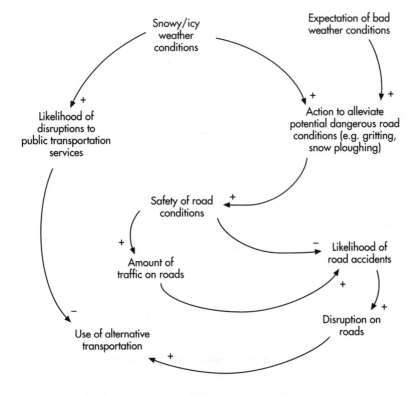

Figure 3.15   Example of a developed causal loop diagram

Using causal loop models for systems dynamics

A causal loop diagram can be used as the basis for developing a systems dynamics model of the problem situation. Systems dynamics involves the modelling of a situation by assigning values to the different levels and rates of activity involved in the problem situation (e.g. the level of pollution, and as a consequence the rate at which media cover of the environment increases). The situation can then be represented by means of a systems dynamics software package in which the program is 'run' over a defined time period and the behaviour of the system noted. The values assigned to different activities can then be adjusted and the resulting behaviour observed. Systems dynamics models can be difficult to calculate, especially where there is some difficulty in assigning a value to a particular activity. However, such models may be usefully employed to aid management decision-making where a mathematical model of the various options under consideration could be produced, enabling the manager to explore these options under different operational conditions. This method of modelling can support a 'What if…?' concept of analysis although, of course, the validity of the outcome depends upon the accuracy of the model and the values assigned within the model. (A detailed description of systems dynamics and related models can be found in Forrester, 1961; Roberts *et al.* 1983; Pidd, 1984.)

BLACK BOX DIAGRAMS

Black box diagrams provide a useful means of representing a complex situation using the notion of 'input–process–output' (see Figure 3.2) which is common to many systems diagrams. The strength of a black box diagram is that there is no need to understand all the processing that is undertaken within the whole system, it is enough to recognize that 'something' happens and that this 'something' has particular inputs and outputs that can be identified. A further advantage of a black box diagram is that by obeying a few simple 'rules' following the convention of the diagram, the process can lead one through a comprehensive learning exercise.

The first stage of the diagram is to represent the whole system (e.g. the organization under investigation) as a single 'input–process–output' diagram. The system is named and the inputs to this system are listed and drawn feeding into the system. The outputs of this system are then identified and shown feeding out of the system, as illustrated in Figure 3.16.

The system identified is then 'broken down' into smaller parts, or subsystems, and the process of identifying the different inputs and outputs for each subsystem is undertaken until a list of all relevant subsystems has been developed. As with the first level black box there is no need to fully understand the processing being undertaken, but when a subsystem is identified it needs to be carefully 'named' in order to reflect

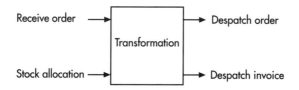

Figure 3.16   Simple first level black box diagram

the way in which the inputs to this subsystem are transformed into the identified outputs. It may be that the activity of the subsystem is easy to name (e.g. a sales subsystem), although at other times it may be useful to move away from the more traditional names (e.g. customer complaint system) and be more accurate in naming the activity (e.g. system to *analyse* and *act* upon customer complaints). At this stage all relevant elements of the larger whole (the organization) should have been identified and it is time to 'fit' the subsystems together in order to understand the whole system. This is not always easy, especially if the analysis has been very detailed. The diagram is gradually built up by identifying how the output of one subsystem forms the input of a second and the two subsystems can then be joined as shown in Figure 3.17.

If the level of detail has not been consistent across the descriptions of different subsystems, problems may occur as it will then be difficult to find corresponding outputs and inputs. This importance of maintaining a consistent level of detail across the analysis is one that is relevant to all systems diagrams, and little advice can be given about how to ensure that this is accomplished (Figure 3.18). All the analyst can do is be aware of the need to maintain the same level of resolution throughout a diagram, and the ability to achieve this seems only to increase with practice. When fully developed, the black box diagram is ideal for illustrating the relationship between the different processes being undertaken within a system. It is important to remember that the inputs and outputs identified for each subsystem may be either a physical input or a flow of information: they are not restricted to data flows as in a data flow diagram.

The production of a useful black box diagram means that the analyst will need to spend time investigating the problem situation that is to be represented in the diagram. The learning resulting from such an investigation is a valuable asset in the analysis process. It is not difficult to see, therefore, that while a diagram can be used to represent a situation to another individual, the process of producing the diagram can be a valuable learning activity in itself.

Furthermore, a black box diagram provides a useful basis from which to develop structured data flow diagrams. Since the black box is concerned with 'systems' that

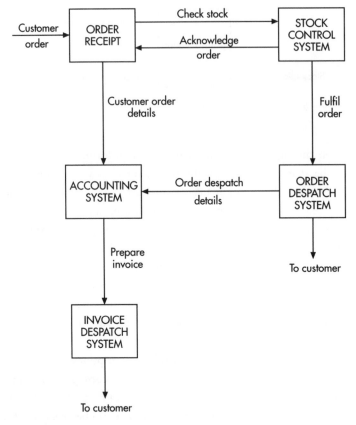

Figure 3.17   Connecting subsystems

must have communication and control in order to function as systems, we may focus upon exploring this communication and control structure as the representation of the flow of data that supports the entire notion. Analysts may find this link between the two diagrams particularly useful when considering the potential role of IT in the problem–solving process.

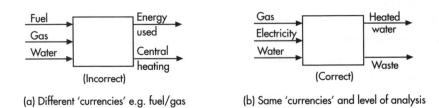

Figure 3.18   Examples of 'correct' and 'incorrect' diagrams

Requisite variety

It is worth pausing at this point to consider the ramifications of Ashby's so called 'Law' of Requisite Variety (1958). Ashby (1978) states 'that if a certain quality of disturbance is prevented by a regulator from reaching some essential variables, then that regulator must be capable of exerting at least that quantity of selection'. In simple terms, Ashby's Law of Requisite Variety is a way of explaining that in order to bring about effective control over any situation, the control mechanism must be capable of addressing all the various outcomes that the situation can possibly develop. In information systems this has a particular significance since it is often the case that to fulfil the entire needs of the clients the technology required would be significant (assuming that such technology is available). It is incumbent upon the ISA to undertake, with the clients, a *controlled devaluation* of the information system definition and subsequent specification. This effectively means that the clients should be made aware of the full ramifications of their stated needs. Too often the technologist may make assumptions about the clients' requirements or be tempted to make rash promises about the technology; either way, this often results in customer dissatisfaction. CLD is intended to be one method of overcoming problems.

RICH PICTURES

Although rich pictures originate from Soft Systems Methodology (SSM), they can be used, distinct from SSM, as a powerful way of recording one's understanding of a problem situation. The notion of a rich picture has been developed into one that takes as its convention a cartoon-like appearance. One reason for using pictures is that it enables one to minimize the constraints that language itself imposes on any description of a situation. The value in being able to do this should not be underestimated since our vocabulary and the way in which we express ourselves contains many nuances and meanings that can be easily misunderstood. This is not to deny the bias that may exist in pictures, but to propose that symbols may reduce the bias and at the same time provide a rich source of information.

In SSM advice is given that rich pictures may be adopted to help illustrate the analyst's perception of the structure, process, climate and power elements existing in the situation under investigation. The diagram is particularly useful for illustrating the overall impression that one gets when finding out about a situation; it is often difficult to put into words but, nevertheless, may prove to be a valuable piece of information about the situation. The ability to include such information, which is often subtle and difficult to define, may be acquired with practice and leads to the production of a 'richer' rich picture.

A common criticism of the approach is that artistic skills are necessary. However, experience suggests that even crude drawings involving matchstick people and

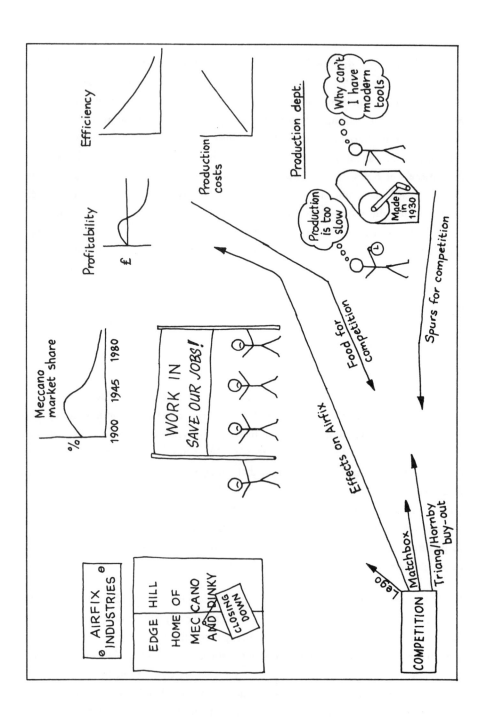

Figure 3.19   Example of a rich picture problem taken from Wilson (1984);
picture from Stansfield (1990)

generalized objects can depict quite complex and revealing situations (Figure 3.19). The best rich pictures are often rough-and-ready sketches that are added to and developed during the process of analysis; they do not have to be neat, beautifully produced graphics but should provide a dynamic working document. However, some practitioners have attempted to use different computer graphics packages in order to produce 'quality' pictures, but this is not recommended since:

- this method fails to capture much of the essence of the picture—the life and spontaneity that is captured within a hand-drawn picture is of great importance and should not be underestimated in the process of transferring meaning and understanding to another, and
- the number of easily accessed graphic images available restrict and limit the richness of the picture (e.g. only certain aspects can readily be illustrated) and there is a tendency for all rich pictures to look the same.

As with all other diagrams, the production of a good rich picture depends upon practice and experience (e.g. by thinking about how best to represent a particular situation and trying it out).

In addition to using the diagram as a means of recording one's understanding of a situation it may also be used as a method of communicating with other people. For example, showing a rich picture of one's appreciation of a situation to a client is one way of facilitating discussion, gaining feedback and validating one's understanding of the problem. Furthermore, a good 'rich' rich picture may contain a large amount of information on one page, which means that anyone looking at the picture can gain an appreciation of the whole situation at one glance—there is no need to read pages of explanatory narrative. On the strength of this 'ease-of-reading' characteristic, the use of a rich picture within a formal presentation may be one way of helping the presenter to talk around a particular area of concern while at the same time enabling the audience to gain their own appreciation of the situation through the eyes of the author of the picture. It should not be forgotten that because the rules for drawing a rich picture are minimal, it can soon be adopted and used by the *client* as a means of recording understanding and appreciation.

Some may feel that the use of cartoon-type representations does not promote a sense of serious intent. Once again, experience has shown that after the initial surprise of finding themselves facing a drawing, most people (even senior managers) soon discover the strengths and advantages of this type of diagram and work with it quite happily.

A potential problem area may occur if the analyst is the sole developer of the rich picture. Although the picture provides the forum for the analyst to record his or her impression of the problem situation, it is important that this understanding relates directly to the analyst's experience within the problem domain. It is all too tempting, as the analyst, to include one's own thoughts and interpretations, which may have little to do with the study at hand. For example, the analyst needs to avoid placing his or her own political interpretations on the behaviour of others. The analyst also needs to take care that the way in which aspects of the problem situation are represented do not cause embarrassment or resentment.

The use of the rich picture provides the analyst with the opportunity to be creative and express situations in a way that cannot easily be done with any other diagram or narrative. It is important that the production of a rich picture should not be trivialized and the rigour necessary in the production of other diagrams applies equally to the production of a rich picture.

Some guidelines for drawing rich pictures are as follows:

- Avoid thinking in systems terms—concentrate upon representing the overall situation.
- Remember that a rich picture is not a flow chart and so does not need to represent all the operational processes in a logical sequence.
- An ability in rich picture drawing can be developed with practice as different ways of representing situations are found and explored.
- Reduce the amount of narrative to a minimum—it is all too tempting to end up representing the situation through a collection of characters within the problem domain who voice their opinions through speech/think bubbles. This approach reduces the potential strength of the picture and encourages the author to revert to expressing the situation in text rather than in pictures.

ACTIVITY MODELS

The notion of an activity model, or as Checkland refers to it, a 'conceptual model', originates, like that of a rich picture, from soft systems methodology (SSM). However, the form of a conceptual model may be usefully adopted elsewhere and we shall refer to it as an activity model to distinguish its general use from its specific use in SSM. An activity model is a form of activity diagram whereby activities of a named system are identified and expressed using the *verbs* of the English language as their main component. The form of the diagram is built around the logical dependencies of the activities involved, with arrows linking the different activities to illustrate such logical dependencies. The activities themselves are placed within cloud–shaped boundaries in order to emphasize that, as a representation of a *notional* system, the activities named are not necessarily real-world activities, they are merely the activities that need to take place if the notional system is to function. In SSM, the conceptual model has traditionally been described as being purely a description of an *ideal type*—that is, developed from a detailed and carefully composed description of a some notional system which is referred to as a 'root definition'. However, practice has shown that we do not need to adhere strictly to the root definition–conceptual model conversion, but instead may produce an activity model directly from some appreciation of the activities of any named system (for example, one identified in a black box diagram). An example of an activity model is given in Figure 3.20.

In order to develop an activity model the system of interest must be carefully named (e.g. expressed in terms of the transformation to be effected together with its associated perspective). Then the next step is to begin to assemble verbs which relate to the activities that must be undertaken in order to achieve the stated transformation. Once these activities have been identified they are arranged by identifying their logical dependencies using arrows to link the activities. A system boundary needs to be included and it is worth while to try to identify the different inputs and outputs of the system (and subsystems). Finally, since we are interested in viewing the named activities as a collected whole, or system, we need to be concerned with the continuity of the system. This can be brought about by monitoring and controlling the overall system, and for this reason it is usual to include the monitor and control activities within the overall system boundary.

STRUCTURED METHODS AND OBJECT-ORIENTED ANALYSIS

In Chapter 1 we highlighted the fact that humans divide a complex world into artificial domains of expertise in an attempt to make sense of it. It is worth reminding ourselves that in trying to address 'real world' problems through the application of computers we must not lose sight of the fact that what we are doing is attempting to simplify reality. In the role of the ISA, we do this through a process by which we translate what is perceived to be the problem into an IT–based 'solution'. This book is not about programming or providing a definitive guide about any specific design methodology, but it is concerned with providing sufficient detail to enable the ISA to link the IT strategy, problem identification and information specification into an appropriate technical design approach (e.g. SSADM, OOD).

It is as well to remember that as we progress through the so–called 'systems life cycle' we are in fact simplifying the problem at each stage. One of our tasks is to produce a technical specification that will fulfil the clients' requirements within the context of

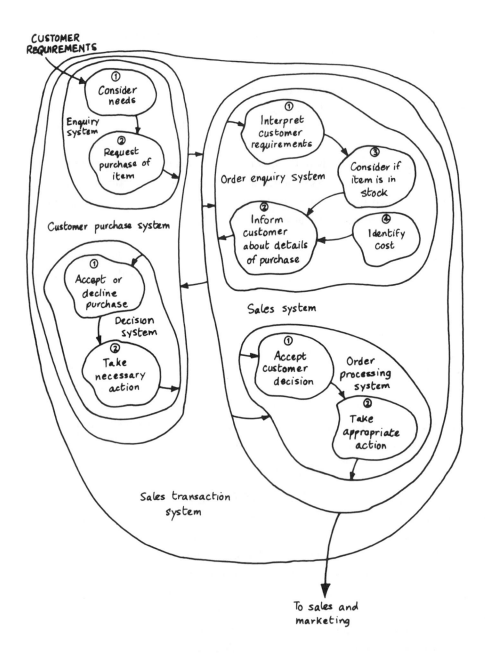

Figure 3.20   Activity model of a sales transaction

feasibility. On this latter point it is important that the clients and the ISA recognize and accept the 'feasible outcome'. In Chapter 2 we proposed an 'information systems life cycle' which is characterized by its iterative nature. Iteration itself will not prevent the problem being oversimplified or the clients being disillusioned, but the process will help to remind them that the 'solution' being developed is a contribution towards making the problem more manageable.

Where IT is deemed to be of value to the clients' management of their problem situation, the ISA should be acutely aware of the complexity of translating the information system specification, Phase II, into a technological form (e.g. a computer-based information system specification). A problem with the production of computer programs (which represents an attempt to engineer the problem situation into a computer-based solution), especially if produced outside the philosophy of CLD, is that they 'hide' the complexity of the problem from the clients. While this strategy protects the clients from the need to have technical knowledge, it results in their having little understanding about what the computer program is doing since all they see is the output without the knowledge of what is happening to the data input. If this scenario is accepted, then the clients cannot be expected to make a critical assessment of their information-processing activities.

As the application domains for the use of computer power have become more ambitious, programs that command the hardware have become larger and more complex, often running to millions of lines of code. The ramifications of this for the management of a project and, consequently, upon the final outcome of a project are many. For example, in large projects no one person can understand the entire program and the sheer size of the task often stifles creativity and forces the re-use of existing software. One way of trying to overcome this difficulty is to develop methods of reducing the amount of code, but this action itself is problematic in that it creates a false illusion of simplicity. Another difficulty is that in order to cope with the sheer size of the task a team of developers is often assigned to it which, in turn, creates managerial problems such as team unity and maintenance of design integrity.

The production of code, which we suggest may form part of the activities within Phase III, results from the 'technical specification', which, in turn, results from the definition of the information system. In CLD we advocate that the clients should have a dominant role in the investigation and modelling of the information system and that this role should be extended through into the production of the technical specification. Clearly at this stage of the design process the ISA will provide the technical expertise but the development of the specification itself should be in a form that the clients can easily follow.

The ISA has two problems to contend with. First, it is necessary to represent the information system in a way that is suitable to client participation, and, second, appropriate aspects of the definition of the information system produced need to be decomposed into a form that is suitable for the production of computer programs. A complex software system has many interacting parts and the most efficient way of managing the program is to reduce it to small parts. Each part can be derived from the key abstractions from the problem situation and we decompose these into a form that will ultimately translate into a program. Two important methods of decomposition are algorithmic and object-oriented, and we leave the choice of method to the judgement and preference of the ISA. It is sufficient to remind ourselves that whichever method is chosen the outcome of the design will be influenced by the method itself.

Structured diagrams

Over the past decade a number of structured approaches for the representation of data-processing systems have been developed. There is little doubt that these methods have brought discipline to the design process and reduced potential errors. Moreover, the automation of the methods through applications generators has made a significant contribution to the final result and reduced further the error rate. Structured Systems Analysis and Design Method (SSADM), among the most popular of the structured methods, provides the practitioner with a complete method of data definition but, like all of its genre, it is concerned with data description not problem definition. Many of the structured methods used owe their origins to the so-called 'forms-driven' methods of the 1970s as illustrated in Figure 3.21.

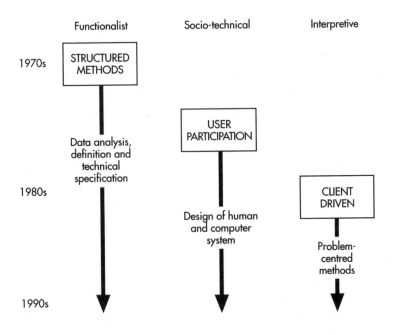

Figure 3.21   'Conceptual' origins of structured methods

A number of structured methods are available to the practitioner, which makes the choice of any one method a difficult task. We do not commend any particular method, but suggest that all can be used in the way we describe here: the essential condition is that they can be adopted and applied within the ethos of CLD.

Notwithstanding the criticism of preserving the status quo, structured methods do enable a detailed description of the flow of data throughout the enterprise to be represented. We argue, therefore, that a structured method which is front-ended by a suitable problem-solving approach provides a powerful combination. In the chapters that follow an example is provided of the way in which a structured method, in conjunction with a suitable systems-based problem-solving approach, was used as the platform for CLD.

The conventions proposed by the Gane–Sarson structured method will be adopted in the examples shown in this text (Gane and Sarson, 1979) but there is no practical reason why any other structured method should not be used. For example, it is increasingly common for systems ideas (e.g. SSM) to be used in conjunction with SSADM (McDermid, 1990; Rudman, 1992; HMSO, 1993). We have adopted the Gane–Sarson conventions as a means of producing an 'information system' model of the situation defined in Phase I which can be used by the clients as a vehicle for discussing their information system requirements.

For a detailed description of the Gane–Sarson nomenclature we recommend their text Structured Systems Analysis (Gane and Sarson, 1979; Gane, 1990) and for other structured approaches there is a significant selection of texts and courses available (e.g. SSADM, 1990). The prime reason for including reference to structured methods is to provide an example of the way in which the problem-solving stage (Phase I) can be linked to the technical specification stage (Phase III), through the use of a suitable model at the information systems definition stage (Phase II), and in a manner that is easily followed by the clients.

Object-oriented analysis

Object-oriented analysis (OOA) arose largely to extend object-oriented design (OOD), and OOD is often used with object-based languages like ADA and also driven by the requirements of object-oriented programming (OOP) languages such as C++ and Smalltalk. The method of analysis is centred around the production of a model which is effectively an object-oriented model of the world. The modelling process consists of four major elements, as shown in Figure 3.22.

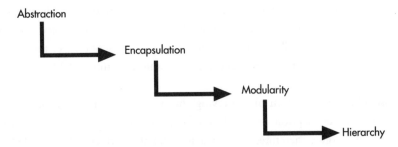

Figure 3.22   The four elements of object-oriented modelling (after Booch, 1991)

The most important stage of any model building is the problem definition stage. We have argued above that this process might be aided by full client involvement which, in itself, necessitates that the form of the model should be one that the clients are able to understand. In CLD we are seeking a direct client input into the technical specification and, consequently, into the design of the hardware and software. The main OOA methods are those concerned with modelling essential object classes and their logical interrelationships. However, we agree with Booch who states that other suitable approaches should not be ruled out provided that they do not constrain development to software design requirements. Booch notes that abstraction analysis offers a mapping between the data flow diagrams of structured analysis and the classes and objects of OOA. OOA   attempts to form a model of the world in which the classes and objects of the problem are identified. From this model the abstractions and mechanisms that enable the behaviour of the model to be represented are, as Booch puts it, 'invented' (Booch, 1991)

The important consideration for the designer is to ensure that the initial definition, or description, of the problem is 'correct'. The more views that can be incorporated and the number of iterations gone through with the clients, the better. We advocate that one of the methods described earlier in this text could satisfy this requirement and provide the input, direct from the clients, into the technical analysis/design stage. In this text we have used a structured approach to the technical specification because this is the most popular method of technical design, and given our belief in the need to ensure a technically 'free' information system definition, this approach can be used in conjunction with the OOD process (by which we mean the translation of the clients' requirements into code).

Perhaps a similarity exists between what we refer to as clients and what Booch calls the domain expert. He suggests that the domain expert is 'simply a user'—someone who is familiar with the problem, but not necessarily the technologist. For CLD, clients are those who are involved in the activities that make up the problem situation. In that sense these individuals are expert within their sphere of responsibility. The intention of CLD to produce a description of the information system requirements, would then seem to be complementary to the basic requirements of OOA.

In OOD the interactions between objects give rise to the behaviour of the notional system. In CLD such behaviour is more usually viewed as emerging from the actions of the activities. Clearly there is a similarity between an active object and an activity and in some cases a clear correspondence is possible. But objects are often introduced during the design to provide services to other objects and so may be more implementation-oriented or low level (as software engineers might say) than the activities of CLD are.

This is not a text on OOA, but we have provided a simple illustration to show the possible relationship between an activity diagram and an object model. If, in the activity model shown in Figure 3.23, the activity 'validate order' uses 'criteria for order validity', then the first activity must pass information to the second and hence indicates the relationship between objects. The meaning of relationships between objects might be found by thinking about the 'validate order' activity in which the

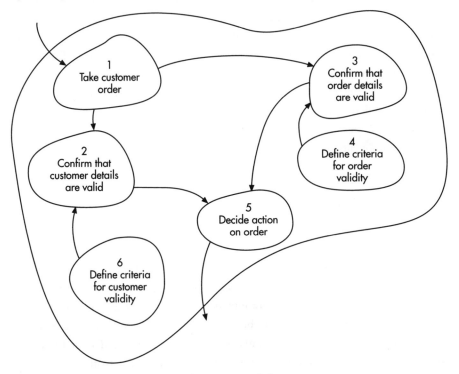

Figure 3.23. Activity diagram of an order validation system

activity itself is composed of a number of actions, such as check production plan, check technical feasibility of order, check customer creditworthiness. From this we have a production plan, technical specification and customer credit. In this case the activities themselves are embodied within the action 'validate order' which, through the process of CLD, can be confirmed by the clients who helped to develop the original diagram.

If we consider the actions related to the achievement of the activity illustrated in Figure 3.23, we might have the following subsystems:

- technical specification
- material requirements
- components.

This list serves as an example of some of the actions involved within activity 4, and fuller details of each activity will be derived from the frequent client/ISA meetings. It is worth noting that the activities themselves will contain actions that might be transferable to a computer and actions that are more appropriate to a human. For example, if the customer was ordering a fuel coupling then the human operator can check certain details relating to the customer (e.g.credit, discount), the order itself (e.g. dimensions, material), but there will be aspects of the problem that will involve human judgement (e.g. potential value of the customer, knowledge of new materials or performance of others). This is another reason why the involvement of the clients throughout the development of the information system is important since the tasks that cannot be translated onto the computer can be witnessed, indeed commented upon, by the clients. If, from the list of 'subsystems' above, we select 'components', we may translate this into an object model, as follows:

Class: Components

Subclass: Fuel Coupling

Attributes: Dimension
Material
Fixing

Clearly, this is a simplification but the example serves well enough to illustrate the argument that has been made above for a link between an activity diagram and an object model. The above diagrams are intended as catalysts for thinking about further research in developing what seems to be a potentially fruitful link between Phase I of CLD and the development of a technical specification in Phases II and III. Fruitful discussions about the relationship of OOD to OOA and object orientation can be found elsewhere (e.g. Booch, 1986, 1991; Coad and Yourdon, 1990; Ward, 1989).

SUMMARY

In this chapter we have provided some examples of tools and methods that might be useful as part of CLD. We do not advocate the use of any particular method but emphasize that any of these might be useful as methods of communication and as means of helping the clients and the practitioner to gain an appreciation of the problem situation. The most important point is that these ideas should be used within the overall framework of CLD, and not as self-contained methods. In Table 3.1 we have summarized the ideas contained in this chapter and suggested where, in the CLD process, they might be useful.

REVIEW QUESTIONS

State what do you understand by the following:

Open/closed loop control	Causal loop diagrams
Feedback (positive/negative)	Activity models
Structured data flow diagrams	Object-oriented analysis
Iconic models	Analytic models
Algorithmic models	Conceptual models
Requisite variety	Rich picture

EXERCISES:

(1) Consider an educational establishment in terms of:
   (a) an educational system
   (b) an employment system
   (c) a local community income-generating system.

   Represent each one in terms of the transformation of inputs into outputs. For example, is an input to an educational system 'students' or 'knowledge' or both? If so, what is the output?

(2) Produce a spray diagram in which you show the logical branches relating to the important considerations that need to be taken into account when considering the purchase of a personal computer for home use.

(3) Use a decision tree to help you decide the course of action you should take when assessing the introduction of an IT-based decision-support system.
   (a) The possibility of purchasing a technology-based decision-support system is about 80 per cent certain.
   (b) There is a probability of almost 0.6 that the decision-support system will be operated on desktop machines.

(c) There is a 60 per cent chance that IT will be accepted by staff.

(d) It is almost certain that the company will chose a centralized machine from which to operate a company-wide management information system.

(4) From the following description produce an influence diagram which includes the labelling of positive and negative influences for the minor loops and the overall effect of these influences on the behaviour of the system.

> The introduction of a company-wide technology-based management information system (MIS) will lead to faster response to customer orders. However, the introduction of IT will enable the company to operate with fewer managers, although if the MIS is successful then the increase in orders will almost certainly enable the company to recruit more staff. Additional staff resulting from an increased order book will be needed in the quality control system which is being implemented to improve the reliability of the product. An alternative strategy to that of installing a technology-based MIS is to recruit more sales staff. A recent survey has shown that for every increase in the salesforce the number of products sold increases by 20 per cent. One problem is that increased orders overload the limited manufacturing capacity, which in turn creates a backlog and often an order cancellation, so care must be exercised to avoid accepting too many orders. Whichever strategy is used, however, the company needs to speed up its order processing if it is to maintain its competitive edge.

(5) From the following definition produce an activity model: 'An information system to aid the decision-taking of a number of managers concerned with the timely arrival and distribution of materials to support the assembly of small domestic appliances.'

A VIEW OF ORGANIZATIONS FOR CLIENT-LED DESIGN OF INFORMATION SYSTEMS

INTRODUCTION

In this chapter we shall explore the concept of a 'business organization' with reference to different theories of organization as presented within organizational analysis and management theory. Thinking about the question 'What is a business organization?' is of fundamental importance to the information systems analyst (ISA) since it is a particular type of organization—the business organization—that is the context in which that person undertakes his or her work. As part of the information system design process the ISA will examine the working practices and procedures of the members of the business organization and take an interest in the way in which information is communicated and controlled within the organization.

In most cases the ISA will take as given the problem situation defined by what might be perceived to be the most influential stakeholder, or what Checkland refers to as the 'problem owner' (Checkland, 1981, 1989a). Often the next part of the process is to attempt to identify how the organization operates. There are a variety of standard approaches to this activity, ranging from the use of organization charts to the application of a favoured organizational model as the means of identifying ways of assessing the effectiveness of organizational operations. The approach taken at the first part of Phase I of client-led design (CLD) needs to be carefully considered since, without care, the ISA may be unwittingly compromised into thinking that the model adopted does actually represent the particular business enterprise. Whatever 'model' of organization is used, this is the model around which the technology-based information system will be designed. Consequently, the ISA needs to have a developed awareness of both organizational investigation and analysis and the relationship of this task to that of the information system design process. In this chapter we shall explore different ways of understanding the nature/character of an organization within the context of the design process.

WHAT IS A BUSINESS ORGANIZATION?

The business organization is the most common environment in which the ISA operates. It is the business organization and the way in which it functions that provides the ISA with the source of information about (a) the processes supported by some information system, (b) the potential contribution that IT may make to this information system and, importantly, (c) the context in which the proposed computer-based information system will reside and operate. We have emphasized the fact that all organizations are unique; even those organizations that belong to the same parent company will have different methods of working and their employees will experience a different 'culture'. This, we argue, is because, in spite of company training schemes to introduce uniformity throughout the organization, staff have different values and norms. Employees will have different views of their business organization and they can act in ways that are not always possible to predict. Moreover, employees exist in a wider cultural system than the work culture that will influence their behaviour. A good example of this, although related to a specific industry, is the work of Goldthorpe *et al.* (1969) in which the influence of the workers' background played an important role upon their attitudes and aspirations at work.

The cultural differences between business organizations is a characteristic which has an important significance for the process of information system design. At the beginning of each project we need to treat problem appreciation, analysis and defini-tion (Phase I) as a new situation to be understood rather than the phase of the study in which the problem is 'solved'. We cannot use the results of one analysis of a business enterprise as if they were a model of another, but instead we should treat each organization as unique and thereby avoid imposing a model that may be in-appropriate.

A second important reason for the ISA to have some understanding of organiza-tional theory can be illustrated by using two prevalent views, both of which attempt to explain the relationship between an organization's structure and the structure of its information system. One argument is that the organizational structure determines the shape of the organization's network of information systems; the other is that it is the information system that determines the structure of the organization. In the first case, such a view places emphasis upon being able to identify an organization in terms of its structure and, hence, being able to understand the shape and significance of the information systems involved. This suggests a view that might be described as a for-mal and somewhat traditional representation of a business organization. The alternative argument is that the information system represents the necessary elements of structure, process, communication and control as well as identifying the inputs and outputs of the 'system' which, together, describe the overall structure of an organization. This latter view would seem to emphasize that the information system is the backbone of an organization: it is the 'skeleton' around which the organization is formed. The difficulty facing the ISA is how to identify the information system, and then to compare this to the way in which the company operates.

The two views illustrate the difficulty of identifying a once-and-for-all model of an 'organization'. Although they represent attempts to describe an organization from an information system perspective, they fail to provide us with any real guidance for information systems design. What we can learn from these two views is the importance of having an understanding of some of the different approaches to thinking about organizations as a prerequisite for organizational interaction. In order to explore this proposal, in the remainder of this chapter we shall review the different organizational models that have emerged from organizational theory in order to identify any models that are particularly relevant to the notion of CLD.

In an attempt to manage our discussion of models of organizations it is useful to have some way of categorizing different schools of thought. The categorization offered here represents an attempt to present different organizational theories from a 'systems' perspective. The three categories refer to:

(1) *goal-seeking models* (a 'closed' system approach, e.g. classical management organizational theory);
(2) *equilibrium models* (where the notion of goal-seeking is prevalent but there is also the recognition of the organization's existence as an open system which seeks to reach a state of equilibrium with its environment, e.g. neo-classical theory through to socio-technical); and
(3) *relationship-maintaining models* (emphasis upon the methods suited to organizational understanding rather than the definition of an organization itself, e.g. interpretivist methodologies) the result of which is that defining the goals and objectives of an organization is not prime but rather how things are, or 'need to be', in order to maintain equilibrium or a 'satisfactory' performance (satisficing).

In this category (3), 'learning' about an organization is seen as a never-ending process. Furthermore, it is the exploration that takes place in determining the goals and objectives that is the important activity since this leads on to an appreciation of that organization's activities. The chronological development and the different areas of concern of our three categories are illustrated in Figure 4.1.

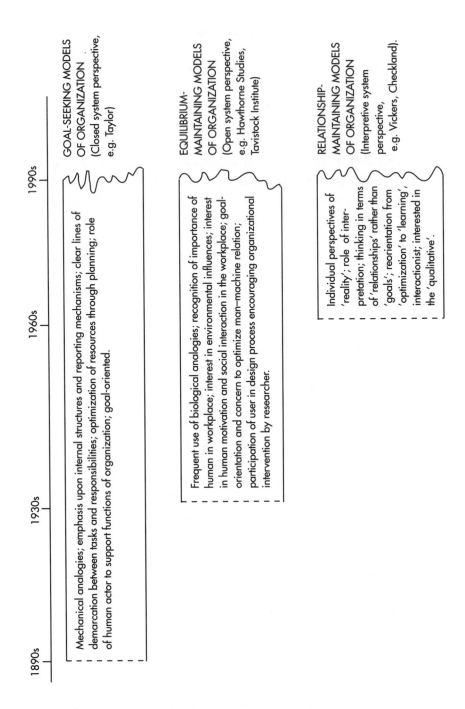

1890s   1930s   1960s   1990s

GOAL-SEEKING MODELS OF ORGANIZATION
(Closed system perspective, e.g. Taylor)

Mechanical analogies; emphasis upon internal structures and reporting mechanisms; clear lines of demarcation between tasks and responsibilities; optimization of resources through planning; role of human actor to support functions of organization; goal-oriented.

EQUILIBRIUM-MAINTAINING MODELS OF ORGANIZATION
(Open system perspective, e.g. Hawthorne Studies, Tavistock Institute)

Frequent use of biological analogies; recognition of importance of human in workplace; interest in environmental influences; interest in human motivation and social interaction in the workplace; goal-orientation and concern to optimize man–machine relation; participation of user in design process encouraging organizational intervention by researcher.

RELATIONSHIP-MAINTAINING MODELS OF ORGANIZATION
(Interpretive system perspective, e.g. Vickers, Checkland).

Individual perspectives of 'reality'; role of inter-pretation; thinking in terms of 'relationships' rather than 'goals'; reorientation from 'optimization' to 'learning', interactionist; interested in the 'qualitative'.

Figure 4.1   An illustration of the three categories of organizational model discussed in this chapter

GOAL-SEEKING MODELS OF ORGANIZATION

The business organization is viewed as a 'closed' system, in which the functional parts seek to optimize goal attainment.

We turn our attention first to our category of 'goal-seeking' models of organization. At the turn of the twentieth century the influence of mechanization in the workplace led to an increased interest in the organization of work practices and associated management structure and behaviour. In an attempt to codify management theory and practice, early theorists (e.g. Taylor, 1947; Fayol, 1949; Mooney and Reiley, 1931; Gulick and Urwick, 1937) took the mechanistic influence even further by adopting the machine as an analogy of an organization. A main concern of early management theorists, therefore, became the determination of human–machine requirements in terms of:

- ensuring that the organization was organized to achieve optimal performance, and
- ensuring that human resources were planned in order to realize this optimization of the organization.

Classical organizational theory developed around a movement towards the mass introduction of technology in the workplace, which helps to explain the emphasis classical thinkers place upon technical and machine requirements and the way in which the workforce is organized to meet these requirements. Embedded in the classical approach to organizations is the importance that is placed upon formal structures and procedures that determine the successful working of the organization. For example, classical management theory places emphasis upon well-established and rigorously enforced regulations, levels of authority, strict reporting structures, supervisory delimitations, and, in short, the bureaucratization of the organization. The classical theorists developed their approach around the view of management as a process concerned with planning, organization, command, coordination and control, and drew upon their own experiences, in particular, from engineering and the military.

The classical management theorist is concerned with the design (in an engineering sense) and management of the organization as a whole within which individual jobs are designed and managed as the means of fulfilling the goals of the organization. To this end, the business organization is seen as a network of functions, such as production, sales, marketing and finance (Figure 4.2). These functional activities, in turn, are identified as a series of interdependent jobs that report to a single manager. This kind of structure exists regardless of the type of organization, whether it be a manufacturing company or a service industry.

Like classical management, the scientific management school of thought also adopts a mechanistic organizational model. Whereas the classical management theorists were interested in the rationalization of management practices and the codification of organizational principles *per se*, scientific management theory was developed specifically around shop-floor activities. Consequently, Taylor's approach to management involved placing emphasis upon the authority of the manager and the adoption of scientific methods in order to plan, measure and assess the most efficient way of achieving the organizational goal. As with the classical theorists, scientific management theory places the organizational worker in a role of supporting the realization of organizational goals and so highlights the importance of selecting the individual most suitable for each job. Training, monitoring and controlling that individual in their employment are fundamental principles of scientific management. Such methods as 'time-and-motion' studies and the detailed rationalization of work practices leading to the division of labour characterize scientific management, and this is reflected in a wide range of organizations from the production-line to the administrative support function. Taylor's work can be seen as representing an attempt to formalize the process of management and give it credibility and respectability through the application of scientific principles. Taylor expressed his underlying intention as one of converting the process of management from a personal skill to an activity that could be called 'a true science, resting upon clearly defined laws, rules, and principles, as a foundation' (Taylor, 1947, p. 7; Burrell and Morgan, 1979, p. 127).

We may usefully view both classical and scientific management theories from a systems perspective to help us identify some of the underlying concepts which we shall later compare with the work of other organizational researchers who were influenced by the systems movement itself. The concentration within this category, then, is upon defining the way in which organizational performance may be optimized either through the use of technology (e.g. by introducing a computer) or by using a mechanistic model of the organization as a means of organizing, monitoring and controlling business performance. With this second approach, jobs can be designed specifically to achieve the optimization that the model 'predicts'. While the organization is treated as a distinct whole or complete entity, little attention is paid to the environment of the organization or to the influence that this environment may have over the organization. For the classical theorist, then, the organization can be seen as a 'closed system' in that emphasis is placed firmly upon the design of internal structures and the desire to identify and apply universal principles of behaviour and operation. The organization is treated as a rational entity that can be tuned to perform at an optimum level of efficiency by the careful planning, organizing, monitoring and controlling of its different functional parts.

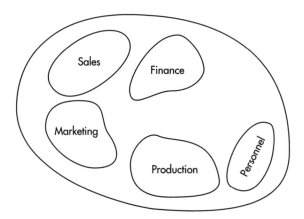

Figure 4.2   Systems map showing the classical view of the network of business activities

GOAL-SEEKING

The goal-seeking model of an organization is powerful and, as such, pervades much of organizational theory and management practice. The notion of goal-seeking also plays a central role in our second 'class' of organizational models, but in order to preserve a clear path in our discussion of these models it seems worth while to discuss the notion of 'goal-seeking' in more detail.

With the 'goal-seeking' approach to organization the effectiveness of the organization's operations are judged in terms of how far the stated goals have been achieved. In order to judge such 'success', measures of performance need to be identified that are suitable for all possible 'types' of goal. When we talk about organizational goals we can think in terms of Schoderbek *et al.*'s three categories of operational, official and operative goals (1990):

(1) Operational goals, which reflect the central activity or primary task of the organization (e.g. production, sales), are the most easy to measure since they tend to be set against quantitative variables such as cost/profit, production numbers, sales achieved.
(2) Official goals, which can be found formally stated in the organizational charter and annual report, tend to be of a more strategic nature in that they serve to express the *raison d'être* of the organization and may often encompass the organization's mission statement.
(3) Operative goals are supplied and operated by organizational members and may be said to refer, at least in part, to the informal goals of the organization (Blau and Scott, 1970). However, it should be remembered that the informal goals may or

may not correspond to the formal goals set by the executive decision takers within the organization (Schoderbek *et al.*, 1990, p. 241). The measurement of these so-called operative or 'working' goals often involves more qualitative elements since a popular way of assessing their fulfilment is either by asking individuals to identify goals that they perceive the organization to be pursuing, or by identifying the goals from observed behaviour of the organizational membership.

As an alternative to the 'generic' type of goals described above, some researchers suggest that the management of the enterprise should identify specific goals. These goals can be set and prioritized according to the way that the organization operates over the period of time allowed within the strategic plan (see Galliers, 1987). For example, there might be specific areas in which managers are directed to control organizational activities that can be best achieved by setting organizational goals and monitoring the success with which they are attained. Organizational activities that might be controlled in such a way are illustrated in Table 4.1.

Table 4.1 Vehicles of measurement for specific organizational activities

Organizational activity	Vehicles of measurement
Strategic planning	Profit targets; return on investment; product plan
Marketing	Strategic plan; competitive situation; strategies and tactics of competition
Sales	Marketing plan; competition; production range
Inventory	Raw materials; finished products; component parts; supplies; work in progress
Production	Productivity; quality; cost; engineering design
Research and development	New products; product modification; product development

MODELLING GOAL-SEEKING ACTIVITIES

A simplified version of the notion of goal–seeking described above may be represented effectively in the form of a control model, as shown in Fig. 4.3. In the model the input to the system (I) is illustrated as feeding into the process (P) undertaken by the system where it is transformed into an output (O). The output of the system is sampled and measured (S) and compared (at C) with the 'desired goal' of the system which has been identified previously. The deviation of the output of the system from the goal is noted and fed back to the input signal so that necessary changes may be made (at A).

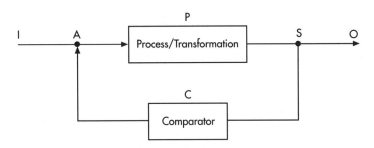

Figure 4.3   The notion of goal-seeking expressed through a simple control model

This basic control model can be used quite successfully to illustrate organizations or subsets such as the 'sales' function of an organization. In Figure 4.4 the same control model has been used, but this time it has been applied to the sales function of an organization.

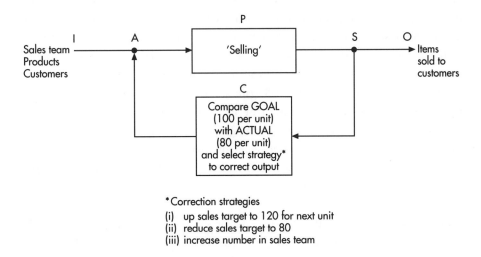

Figure 4.4   The sales function represented as a control model

QUESTIONS ARISING FROM GOAL-SEEKING MODELS

Such a simple model may be developed further to explore the actions that may be taken in order to attain the goal. However, the model can be used to illustrate points raised by different organizational researchers concerning the goal–seeking model of organizations. For example, from the 'sales' model shown in Figure 4.4, a potential way of seeking to achieve the organizational goal is to review the goal set since practice may show the goal to be unrealistic. A question that may follow this, then, is which goal should be sought? The goal to achieve sales of 100 per unit may need to be adjusted as a result of a sudden boom in production or a drop in the size of the sales team. Furthermore, 'sales' and 'production' may have different organizational goals. If so, how can they both be realized?

Not surprisingly, therefore, the definition and attainment of organizational goals can be a source of conflict among the organizational membership. A conflict of interest between individuals (e.g. manager or shop-floor worker) or groups (e.g. sales and production, or even teams within the sales function) may encourage coalitions where some individuals may feel that their goals can be attained by recruiting aid from other members. Alternatively, members of the organization might group together because they feel threatened by the goals that may have been set without consultation (Blackler and Shimmin, 1984; Cox, 1987; Stowell, 1989).

THE GOAL-SEEKING VIEW OF ORGANIZATIONS AND THE ISA

As far as the ISA is concerned, the goal-seeking view of the organization is problematic in that there is an assumption within the approach that there exists an organizational goal, or set of goals, that can be obtained from a representative of the enterprise. In this instance we take a goal to be 'a desired state of affairs that the organization attempts to achieve'. It is difficult to sustain an argument which attributes a goal to the organization since, if we accept that 'organizations' exist as a manifestation of human purposeful activity, then the notion of an organization as a single entity, with consciousness to allow reflection and learning, is unacceptable. Thus the 'organization' cannot have goals. As far as 'desired states of affair' are concerned, these must be desired by someone, or a group, who desires that a particular goal is achieved through the workings of the organization.

This is a difficult area for the ISA since he or she must discover the source of the statements concerning organizational goals. An organizational decision maker may be concerned with the official goals determined by members of the executive board, or by the line management, but the 'organization' itself may be subjected to a variety of other goals. For example, informal, but nevertheless important, goals set within the organization may be the staff's desire to preserve their jobs, to receive a high income, to preserve the status that goes with a position of authority, and the desire to be well trained in order to be attractive in the job market. Informal goals may also play an important role at a high level of management, such as the board's aim to promote the company image as one that supports the local community or to be seen as a company conforming to and even taking the lead in environmental issues. It is important to remember that the organizational researcher may also be influenced by the way in which he or she has been trained to undertake research which, in itself, may influence the outcome of the investigation. For example, training as a computer scientist is likely to lead one to a different approach to information systems analysis and design than if one had been trained in information systems and had adopted the philosophy of CLD. A further factor that should be taken into consideration is the wider cultural social system of which the ISA is a part and which may be alien to the culture and stated or unstated goals of the organizational membership.

The practicality of identifying an *agreed* set of goals, or even deciding whether an organization actually has goals, has been a topic of much debate by organizational researchers. For example, Cyert and March (1963) suggest that individuals alone, and not collectives, have goals and that to define a theory of organizational decision-making one apparently needs at the organizational level something analogous to individual goals. In an analysis of Cyert and March's view of an organization, Pugh *et al.* (1980) maintain that an organization can be seen as 'an adaptively rational system adapting and responding to a variety of internal and external constraints in arriving at decisions'.

More recently, Tsoukas has advocated that social phenomena (of which the so-called goal-seeking organizational model is an example) does not have an existence independent of an actor's account of them. He maintains that organizations operate as a collection of 'linguistically mediated events and processes which change when actors' interpretations change' (Tsoukas, 1993). To summarize this point: as the observer's view of his or her subject changes, so too will the way in which this observed phenomenon is described.

Such arguments as those put forward above help to demonstrate the type of criticisms aimed at the views of organization that we have placed under this goal-seeking category of models. Perhaps one positive outcome of our goal-seeking models is that the conflicts of interest that seem to emerge from the goal-setting process appear to be an enabling factor for those involved. For example, the very process of discussing and (dis)agreeing upon 'goals' sets a wider agenda from which a variety of important topics may emerge such as the conflict between individuals and the formal organizational goals and between the stated and the implied goals.

A further question to be raised about goal-directed models of organization is that not only may different goals conflict but they may also be expected to change continually. With the recognition of the organization as an open system we may view it as operating within a turbulent environment in which it is subjected to a variety of influences (Stowell, 1989). Some of these influences are due to environmental changes (e.g. recession), while other changes result from internal events (e.g. change in personnel).

The formal goals of the organization may stay the same but the way in which the goals are attained may change. Conversely, the various organizational influences may alter the goals themselves (e.g. a change of influence caused by a change in individual coalition).

The notion of a constantly changing environment may be seen as offering both threats and opportunities and it is the manager's responsibility to identify and implement ways of enabling the organization to adapt to changing circumstances. As discussed above, the need to change means that the goals themselves are continually changing which, in turn, means that a mechanism to assess and update goals is required. The need for rapid feedback on the effectiveness of goal achievement and the relevance of the goals to the operation of the enterprise is of paramount importance to the organizational decision makers. It is also an area of increasing relevance to the ISA since it is through information technology that such feedback may be timely obtained. It is the changing circumstances of the organization coupled with the dynamic and complex web of relationships represented by the 'organization' that present the ISA with a daunting task. It is not difficult to see how a goal-directed information system design may soon become obsolete if the computer-based system has been developed too closely around a predetermined set of organizational goals. A useful example of the changing business environment can be found in the production and subsequent sale of goods. While it might be detected that the time span between production and sales indicates the possibility of a quick turnover (Erlichman, 1992 (a), (b) and (c)) such speedy provision of information promotes the need for (a) a constant revision/appraisal of organizational goals as well as (b) a revision of the data-processing system itself.

In cases where a large number of goals are used to model and judge organizational performance the ISA's task is likely to become increasingly difficult: the greater the number of goals, the greater the number of influencing factors to be taken into consideration and the greater the tendency of the 'system' to oscillate if action is taken without due regard to the organization as a whole. Early examples of multiple goal models include Steers (1975), who proposed 15 different operational definitions, and Campbell (1978), who suggested 30 possible indicators of organizational effectiveness.

A CRITICAL REVIEW OF GOAL-SEEKING MODELS OF ORGANIZATION

Using Burrell and Morgan's framework (1979), classical and scientific management can be regarded as being firmly rooted in the functionalist paradigm. To paraphrase Burrell and Morgan, those advocating these approaches treat organizations as if they are part of the world of natural phenomena. This natural world, which is characterized by a single, concrete, universally recognized view of reality, exists and behaves in accordance with universal laws which can be identified and managed in order to optimize performance. Irregularities are recognized to exist but these, too, can be explored and rationalized so that they can be addressed. The behaviour of organizations, like that of the natural world, is dictated by cause and effect, and understanding of this phenomena plays an important role in managing organizations. The role of the worker is a passive one in that the individual supports and reacts to a given situation. In this way, human behaviour at work is seen as being a product of the work situation.

A popular criticism of the classical and scientific approaches has been that they lead to the de-skilling of the workforce and the eventual dehumanization of the workplace. A further limitation of the scientific and classical approaches is that they may be appropriate only where there is little interference from the environment and where the end product of the organization is relatively stable since the carefully specified and tightly monitored and controlled working practices are difficult to adjust to changing circumstances. The continuously changing environment of today's business world, facilitated in great part by advanced microelectronic technology, means that scientific and classical management theory may not provide us with the most appropriate models for organizational analysis. Morgan emphasizes this point when he suggests that while classical or scientific style management may be appropriate to the mechanistic age or to mechanistic style organizations, with the increasing use and power of microelectronics other types of organizational models may be more appropriate as new organizational principles are likely to come to the fore (Morgan, 1986, p. 38).

For the ISA the adoption of the goal-seeking model presents a number of deficiencies both at the design stage and post-implementation. In Chapter 2 we proposed that most information systems analysis methods are rooted in the same kind of philosophy that the goal-seeking model seems to satisfy—namely, the functionalist paradigm—and that these methods are inappropriate and unsatisfactory. We suggest, therefore, that the ISA should consider an alternative method of organizational analysis—one that attempts to take in a wider appreciation of the environmental factors in which the enterprise operates. It is this recognition of the wider context that will enable the ISA to gain a better understanding of the information systems that might satisfy client requirements.

EQUILIBRIUM MODELS OF ORGANIZATION

Equilibrium models involve the notion of goal-seeking together with the recognition of an organization's existence as an open system in which it seeks to reach a state of equilibrium with its environment.

The views of organization that we place under this heading represent a switch in emphasis from the concentration upon the internal structures and processes towards an increased interest in the role of the human player in the organization. The concept of organization also changes from one of a 'closed' system, which has no relationship with its environment, to that of an 'open' system where resources are input and then transformed into the output of the system. The recognition by researchers of the need to consider the context of the system of interest and the relationship between the system and its environment represents the influence of systems thinking in organizational analysis. Our category of 'equilibrium' models is offered in an attempt to highlight this significant change in organizational thinking and also to emphasize the growing concern with maintaining a stable relationship between the organization and its environment. However, it is important to remember that our use of these categories is to help us discuss organizational theory from a systems perspective rather than to imply that systems thinking provides the basis for the organizational models discussed under this heading.

'OPEN SYSTEMS' THINKING

Open systems theory is concerned with the definition of a system in terms of its optimal characteristics. The systems researcher has often been concerned with the identification of a system's characteristics which would help the enquirer to make sense of the complex world in which we live through the employment of a meta-model, namely the notion of a 'system'. Concepts and ideas from open systems thinking have been adopted and incorporated into a number of organizational perspectives. For example, Silverman (1981) has highlighted the influence of open systems thinking in human relations theory, the socio-technical perspective, organizational psychology, structural functionalism and decision-making theory. It is not our intention to provide a detailed analysis of these ideas but instead to draw the reader's attention to the wealth of literature that supports what can be referred to generally as organizational 'open systems' theory. As we shall see, open systems thinking has significantly influenced the ways in which we think about organizations and the way in which we set about organizational intervention (e.g. of the type we take when designing information systems).

Figure 4.5 highlights the difference between the 'closed' and 'open' system perspectives. With the open system perspective the system exists within an environment from which it is separated by a boundary. Resources are input to the system across its boundary and then transformed by the activity of the system into an output which is passed into the environment across the boundary. The output of one system may provide the input to another system. In this model of an organization the environment influences the organization although the organization has little or no direct influence over the environment. Within this open systems framework many of the schools of thought that we may place within this categorization have at their core the notion of goal-seeking and goal attainment. Consequently, the notion of optimizing organizational performance is still of utmost importance. This perspective has the additional element that organizations are viewed as the product of the natural world, a stance which is supported by the theorists' frequent use of biological analogies when modelling organizations (e.g. see Morgan, 1986).

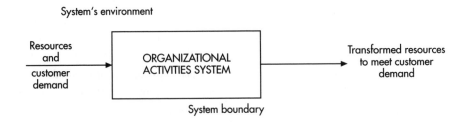

Figure 4.5   The organization as an open system

However, a fundamental difference between the closed systems view of organizations (as represented in our goal-seeking models of organization) and that of the open systems theorists (represented in our equilibrium category) is represented by the shift from the view of organizations as a set of structures to that of the organization as a continuous process. In summarizing the characteristics of the open systems approach to organizational analysis we may highlight the following key concerns:

- interaction between a system and its environment
- goal attainment
- general measures of organizational effectiveness
- common concepts to discuss organizational components and behaviour (e.g. systems concepts).

The open systems perspective conceives an organization in terms of its internal 'systems', both public and cultural, including the formal activities such as financial and sales systems and the needs of individuals and groups in terms of the organization as a whole. Furthermore, the organization, as a system, depends upon the wider environment for its continued existence. From this concept of the need to develop a stable relationship between the organization and its environment comes what we term the 'equilibrium model of organization'.

Barnard's notion of an organization rests upon the two ideas of cooperation and equilibrium. He explains:

> The survival of an organization depends upon the maintenance of an equilibrium of complex character in a continuously fluctuating environment of physical, biological and social materials, elements and forces, which calls for readjustment of processes internal to the organization. (1938, p.6)

Through this description, Barnard's use of systems concepts points to the influence that early 'systems' work had on his theory of organization. Barnard saw the organization as 'a cooperative enterprise of individuals in pursuit of a common purpose ... [which] ... is essentially "unitary" in nature' (Burrell and Morgan, 1979, p. 149). The notions of cooperation and purpose can be seen to play a major role in Barnard's work and they are offered as mankind's natural behaviour. Emerging from Barnard's view of organizations is the role of the 'executive'. The executive is the control mechanism in the organization that seeks to ensure this natural state of equilibrium through monitoring and correcting the behaviour of internal factors and environmental pressures. The actions of the executive may involve the manipulation of the situation and the individual—a point that has been interpreted by critics as being contradictory behaviour if we accept that cooperation is natural behaviour. In spite of the apparent inconsistencies within Barnard's work he is mentioned here as one of the first organizational researchers to attempt to argue and present a theoretical foundation to organizational analysis and the models it adopts. His work is also representative of the move away from concentrating upon the structures of the organization towards a preoccupation with the relationship between individuals within the organization, and his influence can be seen in the work of others (e.g. Simon's work in organizational decision-making and communication (1957) and Cyert and March's (1963) administrative model).

Neo-classical organizational theory, as characterized by the Hawthorne studies in the 1930s and 1940s, attempted to extend classical organizational theory concepts to include social and human dimensions. In this way, the informal, personal and dynamic relationships within the organization were considered as well as aspects of individual behaviour. It was discovered that there were additional features within the workplace that could affect working performance, such as the layout of the working space, temperature and lighting, as well as the 'social conditions' of the work environment such as the relationship between the individual and his or her peers and supervisor, and the boredom or monotony associated with the work task (e.g. Goldthorpe *et al.*, 1968). Perhaps even more interesting was the observation that the very presence of the organizational researchers seemed to influence the behaviour of the workforce. Within the Hawthorne studies attempts were made to review worker discontent and unacceptable work effectiveness from a more personal standpoint. In this way the workers were also considered in terms of their personal lifestyle, including their out-of-work social conditions, and their physical and social conditions in the workplace. In terms of the equilibrium models of organization, the Hawthorne studies saw the individual as a further factor that could influence the overall behaviour of the organ-ization and, therefore, as another aspect to be considered and controlled. The Hawthorne studies represent an early attempt to view the organization as a system of interrelated components of which the human element was a distinct part. Organ-izational concepts illustrated in the Hawthorne studies were developed into what became known as Human Relations Theory (e.g. Maslow, 1943; Herzberg et al., 1959). This collective work set the groundwork for future developments in the socio-technical systems approaches to organizational analysis and also for the action research work that came out of the Tavistock Institute.

It has been suggested (Burrell and Morgan, 1979) that much of the most interesting and revealing outcomes of the Hawthorne studies were not, in fact, analysed and taken into account until after the studies by researchers such as Bamforth, Emery and Trist at the Tavistock Institute (see Pugh et al., 1980). The aim of the Tavistock Group was to explore the relationship between production technology and the social factors of the workplace in an attempt to determine concepts and establish models to represent this relationship and aid its management. It is important to stress that the Group developed a method for undertaking the research in which intervention by the organizational researcher in the workplace was carefully planned and monitored, with the researcher attempting to understand through observation and first-hand exper-ience. A more detailed discussion of the action research approach to organiza-tional analysis and its contribution to CLD of information systems is offered in Chapter 5.

The Tavistock Group's focus of interest was to try to improve the problem of job de-sign within the workplace by exploring the skills of the individual worker and then planning the use of available skills to meet the demands of technology. The work of the Tavistock Institute and that of Kurt Lewin (who was pioneering similar organiza-tional research in the United States), provided the basis for the socio-technical tradi-tion of organizational theory which was to include such approaches as the Quality of Working Life (Davis and Cherns, 1975), and ETHICS (Mumford and Weir, 1979) which provides a framework for the participation of employees in the design processes and the management and implementation of change. While such approaches build upon the tradition of the Tavistock Group the end products reflect different emphases although the notion of 'marrying' technical demands to individual skills can be seen to underlie many of the methods and models placed within the socio-technical tradition of organizational theory.

The term 'socio-technical system' was first used by the Tavistock Institute in an attempt to describe the interaction of technology and social factors in industrial production systems. The work of the Tavistock Institute was heavily influenced by a psycho-analytical perspective which focused upon the importance of group relationships among workers. Consequently, the working group began to be seen not as separate technical and social systems but as a mutually dependent socio-technical system. The notion of a single socio-technical system has had a major impact upon developments within the field of job design and the Quality of Working Life movement.

CYBERNETICS

Within the category of equilibrium models we can place an approach which draws upon the human brain as a model of organization, namely, cybernetics. Beer's Viable Systems Model is a useful example of a cybernetic view of organization. His neuro-cybernic model (1972) focuses upon the cybernetic principles of communication and control as a means of structuring and managing complex systems. Beer's original model can be seen as an attempt to take a 'natural' model, which could be argued to behave in a predictable way according to natural laws, and to use this model as a method of analysing organizations and highlighting necessary hierarchical, communication and control elements of the organization. The recognition by some researchers that the model has tended to be treated as a template around which an organization can be moulded, or forced, has led to an attempt to develop the model using concepts and methods borrowed from interpretive systems thinking (Espejo and Harnden, 1989). Two important applications of Beer's model in organizational analysis are (a) to provide a well-defined framework around which to develop hierarchical communication and control structures within the organization and (b) to use the model as a means of investigating the efficacy of the communication and control structures within the organization. Through the use of the model, optimization of performance is sought by ensuring the presence of those activities that are held to be central to the notion of 'organization'. The concept of equilibrium is supported by the model's recognition of the need to maintain a stable state within a given environment and that the key factor in achieving this equilibrium is the management of the communication and control activities.

RELATIONSHIP-MAINTAINING MODELS OF ORGANIZATION

Relationship-maintaining models retain the open systems perspective but represent a shift in *emphasis from optimization and the maintenance of equilibrium between a system and its environment towards **learning** and adapting to maintain a relationship with the environment on a constantly changing basis. More importantly, ideas that are placed under this category of approach attempt to represent the system of interest and its environment from the perspective of those involved within the problem situation.*

The fact that the majority of models of organization have been developed from within what Burrell and Morgan refer to as the functionalist paradigm can be seen as a historical legacy: it has arisen as a result of people's attempts to inquire into the world about them and so has been primarily influenced by the concepts of scientific method (Winograd and Flores, 1986). However, this last category of organizational model reflects the work of researchers and commentators who have attempted to utilize a different starting position for the basis of their approach to inquiry which seems fitting to the study of organizations as human activity systems. The ideas discussed in this category are different to those in the previous two in that they do not attempt to establish 'models' (as represented through pictorial representations or a framework for *intervention* such as that offered by participative information system analysis methods) of organization. Instead, they provide the theoretical basis, or epistemology, for thinking about organizations as being representations of purposeful human activity rather than as some concrete embodiment of a set of agreed goals. Furthermore, the ideas presented here can also be seen as providing a framework for organizational *interaction*. The ideas put forward under this last category offer the appropriate support and foundation for the concepts of CLD of information systems.

INTERPRETIVE SYSTEMS THINKING

Throughout this text we have advocated the use of systems ideas and tools as a vehicle through which the information systems analyst can support the clients in (a) exploring and representing their information systems and in (b) discussing the ramifications of their requirements. In many respects the ideas and tools we have put forward are offered as a means of enabling all those involved to discuss the domain of interest and, consequently, improve their appreciation of the problem situation. What we need to add now is a 'philosophy' that provides the contextual underpinning for the use of these tools and techniques—that is, the conceptual basis in which the use of these systems tools is embedded. To this end, interpretive systems thinking is offered as providing this theoretical basis.

'HARD' (FUNCTIONALIST) AND 'SOFT' (INTERPRETIVE) SYSTEMS THINKING

In the previous chapters we have pointed out that the systems epistemology has within it two main streams of thought: 'hard' and 'soft' systems thinking. 'Hard' systems thinking can be equated with the functionalist paradigm and soft systems thinking with what Burrell and Morgan (1979) refer to as the 'interpretive' paradigm. In this section we wish to advocate the use of ideas that can be located within the interpretive paradigm as a suitable basis for the type of organizational interaction that is 'client-led design'.

The systems approach to organizational analysis has been criticized by Morgan (1986) who suggested that the perspective leads to a view of organizations and their environment as being fixed and immutable. The criticism proposes that the approach is well suited to the investigation of the natural world but less so when investigating organizations and their environments since these, Morgan (1986) reminds us, are socially constructed and not concrete entities that exist 'out there':

> organizations are very much products of visions, ideas, norms, and beliefs, so that their shape and structure is much more fragile and tentative than the material structure of an organism … organizational environments can also be seen as being a product of the individuals, groups, and organizations who populate them. (p. 74)

Systems theory, as represented in the early systems literature, might be justly criticized by Morgan in this way but over the past 20 years there have been significant developments in systems thinking, particularly in the UK (Vickers, 1965; Checkland, 1981). There is evidence to suggest that early systems theory and practice was influenced by objectivist scientific thinking, the result of which we have referred to earlier as hard systems thinking. While not criticizing this perspective, it is important to recognize that it does appear to subscribe to a positivist outlook which is incompatible with some areas of organizational inquiry and, certainly, with the ideas that we have expressed about client-led design.

Hard systems thinking takes organizational objectives as given (Checkland, 1981). The objectivist stance of such an approach presupposes that the physical world consists of entities and structures that are independent of the observer. Consequently, a hard systems approach may be perfectly adequate when confined to organizational problems that can be clearly defined but are less successful when they are used to address what we may call soft, or ill-structured, problems, and, in particular, problem situations which involve human interaction. While the hard systems perspective tends to view organizations as 'static' and identifiable, the view that takes organizations to be human activity systems (Checkland, 1981) sees the organization as a rich mixture of what we may refer to as 'objective reality' and the interpretation and creation of that 'reality' by those who are part of it.

The mixture of objective and interpreted 'reality' means that the systems perspective we embrace needs to be one that can take the nature of this situation into account. 'Soft' systems thinkers are still concerned with problem identification and solution, but they place increasing emphasis upon the process of *problem appreciation*. Consequently, they recognize that in human social situations this process of appreciation can best be facilitated by providing a framework for organizational inquiry and *learning* (as opposed to a problem-solving technique), and thereby enabling appreciation to take place. A second important point for the soft systems thinker and practitioner is that, as a result of this belief in socially constructed reality, there can never be a once-and-for-all model of a business organization. Instead, what is required is a framework for inquiry which is domain- and situationally-independent, and by means of which those who make up the organization communicate and debate those issues which together form its character and structure.

A fundamental difference between the perspectives reflected in the three categories of organizational model described in this chapter can be suitably illustrated by Checkland's reference to the shift in thinking represented in hard and soft systems. In a comparison of these two modes of thought Checkland (1985) describes a shift from a concentration on 'optimisation' in the hard systems approach to an emphasis upon 'learning' as represented through soft, or interpretive, systems thinking. Likewise, the first two categories of organizational model described in this chapter can be seen as attempts to model organizational structure and behaviour so that organizational performance may be optimized within an increasing awareness of organizational, social and technical factors. Although these first two categories represent a wide spread of approaches to organizational analysis they can generally be seen as providing *views and models of organization* that can be used in the process of analysing organizations.

A criticism of such an approach is that the production of a model of organization can, in fact, act to constrain one's thinking about the organization by concentrating the inquirer's attention upon viewing the organization in terms of the chosen model. Used in this way, the organizational analysis activity becomes an exercise in model validation through the correspondence of the organization to the model rather than an exploration of the organizational situation.

In contrast to the hard systems approaches and methods of organizational analysis that we place within the functionalist paradigm, soft systems thinking can be located within the interpretive paradigm. In fact, the phrase 'interpretive systems thinking' may be more appropriate to describe the arguments put forward here as it will be easier to differentiate between the philosophy of ideas used rather than the practical (and often limited) use of Checkland's soft systems methodology (SSM).

The interpretive paradigm, according to Burrell and Morgan (1979), is that area of their framework which is characterized by the objective/regulation ends of the two axes. They describe the four paradigms as being mutually exclusive, and draw them as quadrants of a single square developed from the two axes 'objective/subjective' and 'radical/regulation'. However, the difficulties in establishing the location of some modes of organizational inquiry within these firm boundaries, especially when being practised (as opposed to a theoretical concept), has led us to redraw their four quadrant framework as shown in Figure 4.6. The newly drawn representation around a central point can be considered in a similar light to an artist's well-blended colour circle: opposites face each other but the line between adjacent 'colours' is hard to discern. With practice we can say that one colour appears, to us, to contain more blue than yellow, but we still accept that it is green. If we adopt this new conceptual framework then we can represent modes of inquiry such as SSM in a more appropriate manner. For example, SSM may be practised in both a 'functionalist' or a 'radical' manner, depending upon factors external to the methodology such as the analyst's intention, or ability, and the context of the situation. Therefore it may be shown quite correctly as stretching from the functionalist, through the interpretive, to the radical paradigm. It might be argued that Burrell and Morgan's representation and classification of organizational theory is just that: a classification of the theory. However, it seems to be more useful to discuss and 'classify' the theory in practice wherever possible.

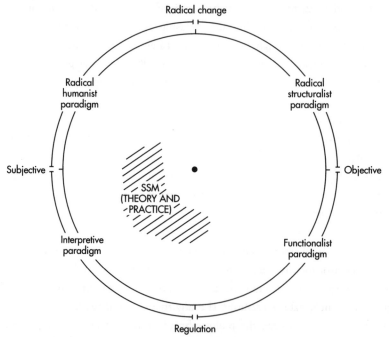

Figure 4.6 The four sociological paradigms (after Burrell and Morgan, 1979)

The interpretive paradigm evolves from a combination of social thought with regard to four main areas of concern: the nature of reality; the nature of knowledge; the essence of 'human nature'; and the nature of methodology (or the process of inquiry).

The nature of reality

The interpretivist perspective of reality is that 'reality' is *perceived* by the individual: 'reality' may or may not exist external to the individual depending upon how far along the subjective axis we travel (e.g. into solipsism), but what is important is the recognition of the process of perception and interpretation that an individual brings to a situation. This has important implications for the inquirer since the inquirer cannot exist completely separate from an area of investigation—the inquirer is part of it. It is important to note that while human actors may disagree upon their perceptions of reality there may be times when actors can share their perceptions or learn to accommodate the perceptions of others. A useful way of representing these ideas is through some of the work of Mary Parker Follet, which is illustrated in Figure 4.7.

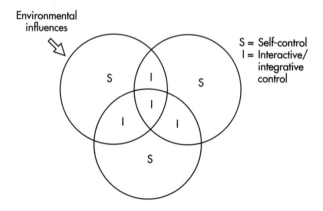

Figure 4.7   The sharing of perceptions between individuals and groups (*source:* Parker, 1984)

The nature of knowledge

The interpretive thinker disregards the realist's belief that universal laws of behaviour direct all social activity. Instead, the interpretivist accepts the individuality of the human actor, including that of the inquirer of human activity. This standpoint emphasizes the uniqueness of any social situation. The stance here is closely entwined with the concept of socially perceived reality in that it involves the recognition by the individual of the socially conceived nature of the concepts and tools that we use when interacting with the world, including the philosophies of inquiry we adopt. To complement this line of thought, the interpretive thinker recognizes the need to be involved in the situation under investigation—that is, to learn from the inside.

The essence of 'human nature'

An important point for the interpretive thinker is that human action is non–deterministic. Humans are seen to have free-will and, in addition, may choose to act in a fashion that may appear to others to be 'out of character', or illogical, or undesirable. In short, their actions form social 'reality' which cannot be predetermined by the inquirer. However, we may also accept that humans are influenced and directed in some part by their personal environment and perceptions of reality.

The nature of methodology (or the process of inquiry)

For the interpretive thinker their methodological standpoint supports the three types of assumption outlined above concerning the nature of reality, knowledge, and human action. Consequently, the process of inquiry adopted and the tools and techniques it adopts supports the acquisition and interpretation of socially constructed reality. In a practical sense, this means that emphasis is placed upon (a) allowing and facilitating actors to describe their 'realities' and (b) providing ways of enabling discussion of these 'realities' in order to (c) increase the appreciation of those involved in these 'realities'.

To summarize, ideas and approaches assigned to the interpretive paradigm can be described as being united in their interest to understand the social world 'as it is ... at the level of subjective experience' (Burrell and Morgan, 1979, p. 28).

INTERPRETIVE ORGANIZATIONAL ANALYSIS
VICKERS' APPRECIATIVE SYSTEM AND CHECKLAND'S INQUIRING SYSTEM

The basis of our interpretive approach to organizational analysis can be found in the work of Sir Geoffrey Vickers' notion of 'appreciation'. Vickers attempted to explain the process that humans undergo when they make decisions and act as a result of their decision-making. In his 'academic' work, Vickers drew upon his life's experience in the world of affairs out of which he developed the notion of 'appreciation' and the processes associated with it which constitute an 'appreciative system'.

For Vickers, tangible and intangible events in the world can best be described as an interacting 'flux of events and ideas'. In this way he refers to people's knowledge of the world and its behaviour, their action in it and the results of their own consciousness in terms of intellectual activity. 'Appreciation' for Vickers describes a continual process of learning for an individual (or group), through which the individual develops a personal view of, or 'appreciates', perceived reality as well as developing his or her own 'values' and, hence, 'standards' about that view of reality. Central to 'appreciation' is the individual's ability to select what is personally interesting, an ability which is, of course, a result of previous judgements made about reality and its associated values. In this way our appreciation of the flux of events and ideas (which is augmented by the individual's own action in the world, and in the process of appreciation itself), is in a potential state of change: in other words, an individual's view of reality and the value that the individual assigns to aspects of that reality change through personal experience.

Vickers discusses the notion of appreciation and the appreciative system in detail in his writings but never represented his ideas in pictorial form. However, Checkland and Casar (1986) have used Vickers' writings to produce the model of an 'appreciative system' which is reproduced in Figure 4.8. In this diagram the process of appreciation has been broken down into subsystems in order to explore the overall substance of the 'appreciative system'. At the centre of 'appreciation' is the process by which an individual (or group) selects 'facts' from his or her perception of the flux of events and ideas that represent the problem situation. This selection takes place by virtue of what Vickers calls the individual's 'readinesses' to perceive the relevance of a 'fact' to a situation which, again, are developed from the individual's experience of acting upon previous 'readinesses'. The second half of this 'select and value' subsystem involves assigning significance to 'facts' in terms of the relationships that the individual wishes to maintain.

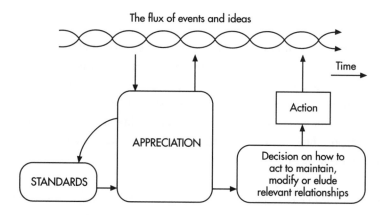

Figure 4.8 A model of Vickers' description of an 'appreciative system' (*source:* Checkland and Casar, 1986, Figure 4)

Before looking at the idea of 'relationship-maintaining' in more detail it is worth highlighting the dynamic activity of the process of appreciation: it is not a once-only event but a continuous process, the previous history of which sets the standards and values for future appreciation, as illustrated in Figure 4.9.

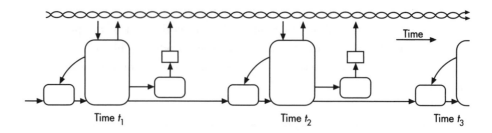

Figure 4.9   Diagram to illustrate the dynamics of an appreciative system (*source:* Checkland and Casar, 1986, Figure 5)

VICKERS' NOTION OF 'RELATIONSHIP-MAINTAINING'

This notion of 'relationship-maintaining' which lies at the heart of Vickers' work and ideas about human decision-making and action requires further discussion since it has given its name to the third category of ideas explored in this chapter. Checkland and Casar have highlighted Vickers' insistence upon the importance of 'relationship-maintaining' as opposed to the notion of goal-seeking as a way of describing human policy-making, decision-making, and, ultimately, regulative action. Vickers (1965, p. 33) explains:

> The objects of our desires and aversion are not objects but relations. No one 'wants an apple'. He may want to eat it, sell it, paint it, admire it, conceivably even merely to possess it—a common type of continuing relation—in any case to establish or change some relation with it. The goals we seek are changes in our relations or in our opportunities for relating; but the bulk of our activity consists in the 'relating' itself ...

Vickers gives a further example to illustrate the subtle but important distinction between goal-seeking and relationship-maintaining. He explains that while goals may be set and attained, they need to be carefully considered within the context of some desired relationship. Failure to consider this is likely to result in short-term action and decision-making which is not well considered in terms of the whole context of decision-making and our attempts to 'manage' (in its widest sense of the word) or 'control' our perceived reality in order to attain a desired state of stability.

> The meaning of stability is likely to remain obscured in Western cultures until they rediscover the fact that life consists in exper-

iencing relations, rather than in seeking goals or 'ends'. The intrinsic confusion about means and ends arises from the fact that no end can ever be more than a means, if an end is equated with a goal. To get the job or marry the girl is indifferently an end, a means and a goal: it is an opportunity for a new relationship. But the object of the exercise is to do the job and live with the girl; to sustain through time a relationship which needs no further justification, because it is, or is expected to be satisfying in itself. (1970, p. 128)

In Vickers' opinion the successful management of any system, whether it be a business organization or one's own personal lifestyle, 'does not consist in prescribing one goal or even one series of goals; but in regulating a system over time in such a way as to optimise the realisation of many conflicting relations without wrecking the system in the process' (1970, p. 116). For Vickers, our tendency to view human decision-making and activity in terms of goal attainment is encouraged, in part at least, by the influence of technology but, we might add, also by particular aspects of reductionist thinking (which has been the legacy of much technological advance). Vickers high-lights three underlying areas for consideration which relate to the goal/relationship maintenance issue (1970, p. 116):

(1) The acceptance of goals as once-and-for-all states to be attained rather than a balanced state to be maintained over time as the overall aim of those who aim to manage and control.
(2) The desire to simplify a situation by reducing multiple objectives to a single goal, which in turn can be assessed by a single measure of success.
(3) The acceptance of 'effectiveness' as the most important criteria for judging the appropriateness of alternatives to achieve a desired end.

For Vickers, then, the acceptance of once-and-for-all goals as a way of planning and maintaining control, the simplification of a situation by developing a single organiza-tional goal, and the ease of qualitative measurement of goal attainment are prime reasons for the prevalent but often inappropriate goal-seeking view of organization. Instead, he offers a view of policy-making and organization as 'the setting of govern-ing relations or norms'. He emphasizes that the difference between this notion of relationship-maintaining and the usual terms adopted (e.g. goal-setting, aims and objectives), is 'not merely verbal' but 'fundamental' (1965. p. 31), if we are to avoid imposing artificial barriers and (implicit) short-term thinking on our organizational activities. Furthermore, he offers a basis for interpretive systems thinking about organ-izations which uses language and concepts that are appropriate and consistent with the philosophy, ideas and sentiments expressed.

THE NOTION OF 'APPRECIATION' AND ITS RELEVANCE FOR ISA

It is important to emphasize that it is not our intention to use this model of the process of appreciation as a representation of how business organizations develop and exist. Instead it is offered as a means of directing our involvement in the process of organizational analysis as an essential part of the information systems provision activity. Vickers' model offers us a description of decision-making and action-taking which is consistent with the interpretive perspective outlined above. It is particularly appropriate to the role of the ISA to adopt such a perspective since it does not limit the view of organization to a single model nor the process of organizational interaction to a set of clearly defined steps. What it can provide is a framework for inquiry; for finding out how those concerned view their organization, or, as Vickers claimed, it may offer an 'epistemology' for exploring, describing and explaining the way individuals and groups deliberate and act.

VICKERS' APPRECIATIVE SYSTEM AS A BASIS FOR CLD

The problem of developing what now might be termed an interpretive methodology for use in organizational problem situations has concerned systems thinkers for some decades. Contributions to systems ideas and practice such as Vickers (1965, 1968, 1970, 1973), Churchman (1968, 1971) and Checkland (1981), Checkland and Scholes, (1990) have drawn attention to the differences between the physical world and the social world and ways in which the organizational problem solver might understand them. While traditional science proposes that the observer adopts the position of objectivity and remains outside the problem that has been observed, the interpretivist position is to accept and explore one's own role in the problem situation. The common criticism levelled at the subjectivist researcher is that of observer bias. However, this is problematic for the subjectivist and objectivist alike since the observer is not only influenced by the situation in which he or she has become involved but is also influenced by the wider community to which he or she belongs. If we adopt Vickers' model, then the observer brings to the problem situation a set of 'readinesses' which direct one's exploration and understanding of the situation and, as a whole, guides and directs the development of an individual's evolving personal perspective, or what Dilthey (1961) refers to as 'Weltanschauung'. Such an explanation suggests that there are no separable social objects or structures, only those that appear as such to the observer.

We acknowledge the work of Checkland in influencing our ideas and in particular his notion of perceived human activity systems as a foundation for a view of organization. Checkland's work is, in turn, heavily influenced by the work of Vickers in which Checkland incorporates Vickers' notion of a relationship-maintaining system. It is this distinction between the notion of goal-seeking and relationship-maintaining and optimization and learning that we feel illustrates most adequately the difference between the functionalist and interpretive views of organization that are summarized in Table 4.2.

Table 4.2   The characteritics of views of organizations stemming from the interpretive and functionalist paradigms

Interpretative notion of organization	Functionalist notion of organization
Relationship-maintaining	goal-seeking
Approach used to learn about situation and is non-prescriptive	Approach used to optimize situation and is likely to be prescriptive
Each organizational situation is unique	Use of pre-validated models encourages view of 'generality' of organizational situations
Recognition of relevance of qualitative meaures of performance	Need to assess organizational effectiveness through quantitative measures of performance
Organization exists and develops over time as a result of its previous history and the involvement of its organizational actors	Organization exists externally to its members although it may be influenced by them
Generally, encourages loosely structured but flexible methods of investigation and analysis which offer an opportunity to learn and then enable more appropriate and selective use of structured methods if necessary	Generally, encourages structured and relatively inflexible methods of exploration and analysis which are likely to be used in problem-solving

REVIEW QUESTIONS

What do you understand by:

Goal-seeking models of organization	Open systems
Equilibrium models of organization	Closed systems
Relationship-maintaining models of organization	Scientific management
Interpretive systems thinking	Socio-technical systems
Classical management theory	Appreciative system
Values and norms	Inquiring system

EXERCISES

(1) (a) Discuss the various coalitions, or social groupings, in your educational institution or business organization and identify their potential goals. Are there any
areas of conflict within/between the 'coalitions'? Are there any coalitions that
share members but have different goals?

    (b) State each goal identified above in terms of some relationship to be main-
tained.

(2) Consider your educational institution in terms of each of the three categories of
organizational theory discussed in this chapter. What effect might each model
have upon the process of information systems analysis?

(3) Describe the difference between a participative approach to information systems
analysis (e.g. ETHICS) and the notion of client-led design.

(4) Describe Vickers' notion of an appreciative system. Explain the process of client-
led design in terms of a process of 'appreciation'.

(5) Discuss the relevance of the relationship-maintaining model of organization to the
notion of client-led design.

5

ACTION RESEARCH:
A METHOD FOR
CLIENT-LED DESIGN

INTRODUCTION

In the previous chapter a view of organization based upon the notion of maintaining relationships and learning was put forward as an appropriate model of a business organization for the practitioner of client-led design (CLD) to adopt. In this chapter the aim is to describe the concept of 'action research' and its relevance to CLD as a way of conducting the subjective mode of organizational inquiry and analysis described in the previous chapters. The characteristics and strengths of action research are highlighted by comparing this approach with the more 'traditional' approach to inquiry, namely positivist empiricism, or 'scientific method'. While this chapter offers a thorough 'academic' argument for the use of action research, it also intends to show how the theory and practice of subjective inquiry can be brought together.

THE POSITIVIST EMPIRICIST PERSPECTIVE

Maturana (1978) offers a useful summary of positivist empiricism which he describes as being concerned with the following main points:

> (a) observation of a phenomenon that, henceforth, is taken as a problem to be explained; (b) proposition of an explanatory hypothesis in the form of a deterministic system that can generate a phenomenon isomorphic with the one observed; (c) proposition of a computed state or process in the system specified by the hypothesis as a predicted phenomenon to be observed; and (d) observation of the predicted phenomenon. (p. 28).

A notion central to positivist empiricism is that situations are 'set up' and an attempt is made to observe objectively the manipulation of variables by value-neutral techniques. We can agree with those who have questioned this philosophy since such an approach does not easily translate to all aspects of inquiry within the social sciences (e.g. Lewin,

1948; Weber, 1949, 1964; Emery and Trist, 1965; Berger and Luckmann, 1966; Checkland, 1981; Reason and Rowan, 1981; Lincoln and Guba, 1984; Winograd and Flores, 1986; Checkland and Scholes, 1990; Jackson, 1991). The following discussion reviews those areas in the practice of positivist science identified by such researchers as being inappropriate when transferred to particular aspects of social science, which we shall take to include the development of computer-based information systems.

THE ROLES OF THE 'OBSERVER' AND THE 'OBSERVED' AND THE NOTION OF 'REALITY'

As Maturana suggests, of fundamental importance to positivist empiricism is the observation of experiments that have been specifically designed to test a given hypothesis. This approach incorporates the notion of the 'observer' as one who is outside the influence of the experiment, and who can control and manipulate variables in the situation being tested in order to be able to define general laws that explain the situation being tested and the overall results of the experiment. This primarily presupposes that the 'observer' is neutral and can, therefore, objectively analyse and manipulate the experiment without influencing the behaviour of the experiment taking place. This stance is consistent with the positivist belief that 'there is one reality and one true knowledge which corresponds to it' (Oquist, 1978, p. 146). Such a belief results in the view that any activity, whether human or otherwise, can only be validated by objective, controlled observation of data—an approach that is adopted in the natural sciences but, as outlined above, has been argued to be inappropriate when transferred to some areas of the social sciences. However, in contrast, the view of social reality adopted in this text is nominalist in that 'reality' is argued to be a product of an individual's consciousness.

In the previous chapter we proposed that the ISA, in addition to technical expertise, should possess the knowledge and skills of the organizational analyst and should expect to assume a role of guiding and directing the inquiry, not by the imposition of models and technological constraints but through the practice of an appropriate mode of inquiry and a philosophy of full client involvement. In a practical sense, therefore, the ISA's intervention into the social setting cannot be ignored since it is most likely to affect the behaviour of those under investigation. It is for this reason that emphasis is placed here upon the need for the analyst to be recognized as a participant in the action rather than as an outside observer (Blum, 1955; Warmington, 1980). Consequently, the analyst needs to recognize and address the problem of his or her own potential for disturbing the 'system' being investigated and for influencing its behaviour.

A second point to be made about a positivist approach is that the 'object' of the experiment is considered as behaving in such a way that it can be generally predicted, and experiments can be designed to enable consistent and repeatable results to be achieved. The difficulty of applying such an approach to the social sciences has generated an alternative view, namely that:

- social systems are non-deterministic and may more accurately be viewed as 'purposeful systems': human actors, therefore, should not be viewed as 'objects' of inquiry but as being capable of making independent decisions and taking relevant action;
- the process of conducting an inquiry in social situations involves not only the intervention into the problem situation but also the interpretation of the situation and the results of the research by the researcher; and
- the analyst may cause those involved to act differently to their normal behaviour (e.g. Mayo, 1949).

In questioning the applicability/appropriateness of these scientific principles when undertaking research involving human actors (e.g. designing information systems within an organizational environment) we may begin to see the significance of discussions and concepts put forward in previous chapters. For example, it has been suggested that Vickers' notion of 'appreciation' is of potential benefit to the ISA since this notion highlights the importance of the individual's, or group's, interpretation of *reality* and the assignment of *value* to that reality.

THE ROLE OF HISTORY

It has been argued that positivist empiricism pays little, if any, regard to history as a catalyst to decision-making and action (Susman and Evered, 1978, p. 586); for example, it tends to assume conformity across social systems. This stance can be contrasted with that of Vickers, in whose work the concept of 'history' (in terms of both events and ideas) is central to the notion of 'appreciation'. For example, Vickers argues that it is through interaction with the continuous flux of events and ideas that actors develop their judgements of reality and value, which in turn enable the individual or group to make decisions about appropriate action (Vickers, 1965, pp. 100-1). If we accept Vickers' argument, then it is fundamental (a) that the ISA (who is effectively an organizational researcher) views each business organization as a product of its own particular history and, therefore, considers each business organization afresh, and (b) that the method of inquiry, design and development (e.g. the method for information systems analysis) takes this view into consideration.

VALUE-NEUTRALITY OF METHODS

Related to the notion of objective observation and designed experiment is the idea of the value-neutrality of methods used to conduct the research (e.g. questionnaires, surveys, personality tests). However, the choice of method used can be argued to have a direct influence upon the outcome of the investigation. For example, a point made by Habermas (1971), and summarized by other workers, explains that 'knowledge and human interests are interwoven, as reflected in the choice of methods and the ends towards which such methods are put' (Susman and Evered, 1978, p. 585). This is an issue that is discussed by Mumford and MacDonald (1989) in relation to the development of expert systems. They warn that:

> It has to be recognised that methods are useful tools that help the systems designer to systematically tackle difficult problems, but they are not neutral. They embody particular visions of the world and incorporate the values of their creators (p. 13).

Furthermore, we must acknowledge that the manner in which we use the methods and techniques is of utmost importance: our use of these approaches can never be neutral since, through our involvement, we bring our own understanding and interpretations to bear upon their application. A potential problem that is precipitated by the recognition of the threat human actors place on any attempt to be neutral, or objective, is highlighted by Susman and Evered (1978, p. 585). They explain that in an attempt to preserve neutrality and conduct a controlled experiment the positivist researcher may be tempted to use methods 'based upon deception and manipulation', which, it can be argued, aside from the ethical issues involved (e.g. Checkland, 1981. p. 39; Punch, 1986, pp. 35–44), can distort the results obtained during the process of inquiry.

The position concerning the non–neutrality of methods and techniques used is not only relevant to organizational research *per se* but also to the way in which the ideas proposed within this text can be utilized. For example, it seems logical and desirable to establish a method of approach that is consistent with and sympathetic to the notion of CLD developed during this text. Failure to do this would result in the application of the ideas discussed in this text and in the monitoring of the use of these ideas using criteria previously argued to be inappropriate to CLD.

THE FORMULATION AND TESTING OF HYPOTHESES AND THE NOTION OF REPEATABILITY

Central to positivist empiricism is the formulation and refutation of hypotheses as a means of furthering scientific knowledge (e.g. Popper, 1959; Plutchik, 1974, pp. 180–1; Schwartz and Jacobs, 1979, pp. 3–4; Checkland, 1981, pp. 50–8). Related to the idea of testing hypotheses is the notion of repeatability as it is only by the repetition of an experiment and by the observation of identical results that 'scientific knowledge', or 'truth', can be established (Checkland, 1981, p. 53). Closely associated with the notion of repeatability is that of measurement since measurement allows values from experiments to be recorded and repeated. Obviously, the more specific and definable the measurement then the more successfully we can compare results. A result of this situation is described by Checkland when he explains that: 'Hence the potentially most powerful scientific facts are those expressed as the quantitative results of experiment' (Checkland, 1981, pp. 54–5). If we consider this situation with regard to inquiry into social systems it presupposes, first, that all human actors behave in identical fashion in the same circumstances and, second, that all aspects of human action can be measured accurately and sufficiently in quantitative terms. Qualitative measurements are far more difficult to deal with and, consequently, recognition of the need to use them is often countered by an attempt to quantify them by further breaking down the elements into definable and measurable chunks (e.g. goals). (However, as levels of quantification increase, then so too may margins for error.)

With regard to the positivist view of repeatability of an experiment, some social science researchers have suggested that the human facility for consciousness and the ability to act at whim, or on impulse, make it difficult to replicate the same situation in research involving human actors as may be achieved in, say, a chemical or biological experiment (Checkland, 1989b, pp. 38–9). Likewise, the inability to quantify human action in all its possible combinations has persuaded some researchers that measurement of human action must be qualitative as well as quantitative (e.g. Lewin, 1948; Weber, 1964; Garfinkel, 1968; Schutz, 1971; Blumer, 1975; Schwartz and Jacobs, 1979; Reason and Rowan, 1981; Lincoln and Guba, 1984; Gill, 1986; Cooperrider and Srivastva, 1987; Stevens, 1990).

LANGUAGE AND MODELS

An aspect of positivist empiricism which we, among others, deem inappropriate when translated to some areas of social science is that 'a system is defined only to the extent that a denotative language exists to describe it' (Susman and Evered, 1978, p. 586). However, as Popper explains, 'all languages are impregnated with themes and myths that are a result of the individual's experience and so contribute to our inability to describe phenomena consistently' (1983, p. 146). The tendency to rely on models to illustrate what '*is*' frequently leads to the use of these models to structure an inquiry that results in the acquisition of knowledge relevant to the model, but not necessarily to the problem situation.

A practical example of the problems of imposing functionalist models on the subject of inquiry was given in Chapter 1 where both explicit and implicit models of analysis were identified as underlying particular approaches to information systems development. Such models were argued to be inappropriate to certain aspects of the task in that they forced the situation into the framework of the chosen method of analysis. A result of this situation is the potential danger that the use of such functionalist models concentrates upon the identification of activities that relate directly to the model used and to the 'reality' that they are *supposed to represent* rather than to the reality *perceived by those involved.*

POSITIVIST SCIENCE AS A PRODUCT OF THE HUMAN MIND

A final, important, aspect of positivist science relates to the problem of failing to recognize that positivist science 'is itself a product of the human mind' (Susman and Evered, 1978, p. 586). This point is emphasized by Popper, who has argued that all knowledge and learning and the method of science 'consists of the modification (possibly the rejection) of some form of knowledge or disposition, which was there previously' (1983, p. 71). The significance of this statement lies in the fact that scientifically proven knowledge generally develops from within its own framework of knowledge, reinforcing its own theoretical foundations and methods. For example, Kuhn (1962), putting forward a point similar to that of Popper's, describes the way in which hypotheses to be refuted in scientific research are consistent with the current accepted state of knowledge which makes any particular investigation meaningful. He describes the body of acceptable knowledge that influences scientific research as a 'paradigm' which, from time to time, undergoes shifts that influence the choice of hypotheses and the direction of useful research. In a practical sense, positivist empiricism seems to have become the *de facto* standard for research into our world, whether natural or artificial, and this can be clearly seen in the field of computing. According to Winograd and Flores (1986, p. 16), this is a direct result of what they refer to as the 'prestige and success of modern science' and the 'deep-seated pre-understanding' of science.

ACTION RESEARCH AS A FRAMEWORK FOR SOCIAL ENQUIRY

The scientific method has been widely adopted in research involving human actors (e.g. within the fields of psychology, cognitive science, management science and computing science). While the philosophy of positivism proposes that 'all true knowledge is based upon empirical data' (Checkland, 1989b, p. 39), there is a body of researchers, following the Weberian tradition in social science, that concentrate upon the understanding of social action based upon the actors' subjective understanding of everyday happenings rather than upon empirical data. Researchers aligned with this strand of thinking have highlighted the limitations that positivism places upon inquiry in the social sciences (e.g. Berger and Luckmann, 1966; Garfinkel, 1968; Schutz, 1971; Habermas, 1972; Giddens, 1976; Checkland, 1981; Lincoln and Guba, 1984; Silverman, 1985). In questioning the appropriateness of 'scientific method' for all areas of social inquiry, some researchers have sought an alternative framework for research that is more suited to the 'interpretive' character of social science. A framework for research resulting from this concern has become known as 'action research'.

Action research can be seen to have two main roots, namely, the work of Lewin at the University of Michigan, USA, and of a group of researchers from the Tavistock Institute of Human Relations in the UK. The term 'action research' is credited to Kurt Lewin who, in 1946, described what he called the process of 'rational social management' which 'proceeds in a spiral of steps each of which is composed of a circle of planning, action, and fact-finding about the result of the action' (Lewin, 1948, p. 206). This iterative activity was offered as a practical means of carrying out the two main concerns of the action researcher, as described by Rapoport (1970, p. 499):

> Action research aims to contribute both to the practical concerns of people in an immediate problematic situation and to the goals of social science by joint collaboration within a mutually acceptable framework.

Although the work of Lewin *et al.* and the Tavistock Institute was in parallel, the influences were different. Rapoport (1970) suggests that Lewin's research was 'more academic in orientation' and had close links with experimental psychology (p. 501), whereas he characterizes the main theme of the Tavistock Institute as the practical need 'to get collaboration from members of an organization while attempting to help them solve their own problems' (*ibid*, p. 500). Disciplines of particular influence to the Tavistock group were those of psychology, social anthropology, psychoanalysis, social psychiatry and open systems theory. In spite of the different starting points of Lewin and the Tavistock Institute, they shared an interest in providing the means of (a) furthering the body of knowledge about social decision-making and action and (b) enabling social science to play a role in the solving of important social problems (Clark, 1980).

Of the various individual definitions of action research that are available in the literature (e.g. Rapoport, 1970; Clark, 1972; Peters and Robinson, 1984; Hult and Lenung, 1980; Wilson, 1984), the one chosen as a means of illustrating the approach here is that of Susman and Evered (1978, p. 588). Their description is adopted because of their attempt to offer a clear definition and discussion of what they consider to be the five basic elements of action research, namely: diagnosing, action planning, action taking, evaluating and specifying learning. Their description of this cyclic process is illustrated in Figure 5.1, which helps to emphasize the iterative process of action research.

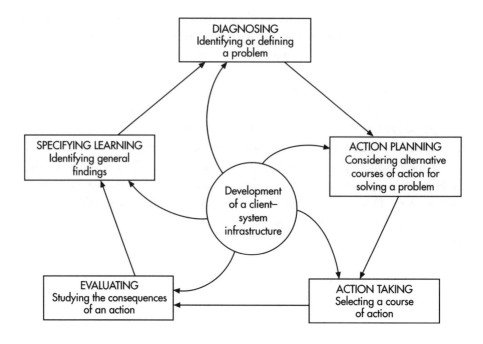

Figure 5.1   Action research as a cyclic process *(Source:* Susman and Evered, 1978)

The process of action research can be described as a method by which knowledge about a particular situation is acquired by an individual or group through the process of interacting with that situation. This knowledge is then used, with the client, to develop strategies for problem-solving relevant to that particular problem situation. The result of the problem-solving exercise is then used to help the process of rethinking about the problem situation and the manner in which the problem-solving was carried out. The cyclic nature of the approach, which can be seen to have parallels with the notion of the hermeneutic cycle (Dilthey, 1961), is of prime importance in that it allows for continual learning and, consequently, represents a major difference to positivist methods of research. This difference is explained by Oquist (1978) who illustrates a fundamental concept of action research when he explains that in this approach the aim of the production of knowledge is:

> to guide practice, with the modification of a given reality occurring as part of the research process itself. Within action research, knowledge is produced and reality modified simultaneously; each occurring due to the other. (p. 145)

Once again, the links between these ideas and the notion of an 'appreciative system' should be clear in that they both describe the continuing development of one's understanding of 'reality', based upon the cycle of previous action and reflection upon this action.

ACTION RESEARCH AS A MEANS OF ADDRESSING SOME PROBLEMS OF EMPIRICISM FOR SOCIAL INQUIRY

As explained above, it is difficult to give an unequivocal definition of action research since different commentators place different emphasis upon various concepts and merits of the approach. However, elements viewed to be central to the research reported here are:

- 'reality' as a social construct
- the cyclic process of theory and practice
- the collaborative learning process that is brought about by the approach
- the treatment of human actors as 'purposeful systems' rather than 'deterministic systems'
- the recognition of the importance placed on the more subjective elements of inquiry such as experience, intuition and hunches.

These different aspects are discussed in more detail below.

'Reality' as a social construct

An underlying concept of action research is the view that 'reality' is socially constructed (e.g. Mead, 1934; Berger and Luckmann, 1966), as opposed to the positivist's assumption of one external reality (e.g. Burrell and Morgan, 1979, pp. 4–5; Oquist, 1978, p. 146). This concept can be related to the earlier discussion, in Chapter 4, of the different ontological and epistemological foundations of functionalist and interpretive views of 'reality'. What Burrell and Morgan describe as the nominalist and anti-positivist views of interpretive sociology can be seen to characterize the views of the action researcher who is concerned with the recognition of the real world as it is at the level of subjective experience.

The theory/practice cycle

A notion central to action research is that of the theory/practice cycle as a means of learning about a situation and acting collaboratively upon this learning in order to solve problems. This iterative process can be seen as offering several correctives to the practice of positivist empiricism described above. First is the idea of collaborative investigation whereby the inquirer and those involved in the problem situation work together to understand the problem situation and then decide how to solve it (Gilmore et al, 1986, p. 162). This stance is an attempt to address the criticism aimed at empirical research whereby the inquirer takes the role of the impartial and objective 'observer' of the problem situation (*ibid.*). In action research the process of intervention and its influence upon the problem situation brought about by (a) the presence of the inquirer and (b) the aims of inquiry, is recognized and taken into account in the research method. Susman and Evered (1978) add that this situation encourages the inquirer to also 'clarify and represent his own ethics and values so that they, along with those of the client system, can serve as guidelines against which to assess jointly planned actions' (p. 589). This point is of importance to the notion of CLD since, as discussed above, the role of the ISA and the purpose of analysis makes the intervention into organizational practice explicit and, in effect, helps to move the information systems analysis process from one of only 'intervention' to one of 'interaction'. Consequently, the aim of the practical phase of the analysis is to learn as much about the effects of the analyst's involvement in the problem domain as about the domain itself.

The theory/practice cycle of action research also serves to place greater emphasis upon the tools and techniques that are used in a problem situation, because the results of their use are carefully considered by those using them. This notion is particularly appropriate to CLD because it aids the clients in understanding the effects of the method of development chosen and the consequences of their actions.

Collaborative learning

A point which relates to the theory/practice basis of action research is the emphasis that is placed upon learning and the way that this is brought about through the theory/practice cycle. Oquist (1978) explains the relationship between practice and theory when he describes the position of dialectical materialism on this point:

> Action by itself is not of value without the consciousness which allows humans to purposely interact with their physical and social environment. Action without thought is meaningless … theory and practice are dialectically related in that they conform a unity of opposites. One necessarily implies the other. (p. 158)

For the action researcher, then, the purpose of theory is to promote meaningful and appropriate action (or practice of that theory), the results of which add to the theoretical knowledge about social theory and to the knowledge about the given situation. This will help to indicate the action to be taken. It is this approach that we advocate as being relevant to organization analysis in that it provides the means of learning about both the problem domain and the use of ideas on a subjective approach to analysis advocated in the earlier chapters. We emphasize the 'learning' activity that the practical phase of organizational analysis offers in raising the awareness of the clients' appreciation of organizational problems as a whole and about the way in which the investigation is conducted. The equal partnership between ISA and clients, with both bringing their own areas of expertise to the debate, is of central importance to CLD.

Human actors as 'purposeful systems'
A further point about action research is that it does not view human actors as 'objects' of inquiry but as 'purposeful systems' that can initiate changes of ideas and action and can choose to behave 'capriciously' (Checkland, 1989b, pp.38–9). This concept emphasizes the individuality of human actors, and of groups of actors, and highlights the need to view each new problem situation as a result of its own context and history. Each problem situation is, therefore, unique and so each approach to problem-solving needs to be freed from previous assumptions about the problem and how it should be solved. An important aspect of action research, then, is the iterative learning about a particular problem situation that is gained through intervention in the problem situation. Gilmore *et al.* (1986) emphasize this point when they explain:

> in the action modes of inquiry the understanding arises out of the exploration of a particular situation and is inevitably shaped by local interests and practical concerns. The primary data in this type of inquiry are derived from experience, and experience is context-sensitive. (p. 165)

A practical example of this point can be found in Chapter 6 in which a study was conducted in the commercial department of a business organization. As the study progressed it was clear that staff had different views about the problem situation, with each set of interviews offering a new problem setting. The lessons learned from these separate encounters helped some observations to be made about the use of the approach that could then be taken into consideration in the next phase of the analysis. Likewise, lessons learned from the next study contributed to the development of the approach adopted in a following study.

Qualitative and heuristic knowledge
Positivist empiricism was criticized above for the way in which functionalist models are often used as a means of generating information about the problem situation to enable problem-solving. Susman and Evered (1978) point out that this approach tends to leave much about the problem situation unknown, which can often be explained through what the actors involved describe as 'intuition, hunch, interpretation, etc.' (p. 586). In recognition of the potential value of such knowledge, action research encourages its exploration and recording in order to offer the opportunity to develop 'a deeper understanding of the organizational values, encourage consideration of new

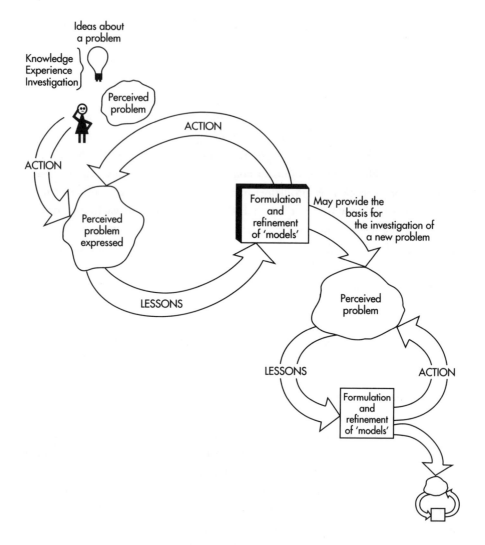

Figure 5.2   Diagram to illustrate the iterative nature of action research showing the hierarchical relationship between the lessons learned within a study and between studies

organizational forms, and facilitate recognition of clues to the new forms the organization might take' (*ibid.* p. 586). Such an aim can be seen as an attempt to maintain the focus of attention upon the total problem situation and its environment (Clark, 1980, p. 153).

In order to achieve this deeper appreciation of a problem situation, those advocating action research emphasize the focus on the understanding of everyday action rather than upon the observation of behaviour in reaction to designed experiments (e.g. Weber, 1964, p. 103; Silverman, 1970, p. 128). For Lewin (1948), the problem of recording the relevant everyday facts and happenings during the theory/practice cycle was one of the most difficult. He describes the diverse type of information that needs to be recorded with reference to a piece of action research with which he was involved:

> It is obviously necessary to record scientifically the essential happenings during the workshop. Here, I feel, research faces its most difficult task. To record the content of the lecture or the program would by no means suffice. Description of the form of leadership has to take into account the amount of initiative shown by individuals and subgroups, the division of the trainees into subgroups, the frictions within and between these subgroups, the crises and their outcomes, and, above all, the total management pattern as it changes from day to day. (p. 210)

Lewin's comment also emphasizes a point made by Silverman (1970), that although positivist science and action research do not share the same perspective they do have in common the 'canons of rigour' (p. 126). In this sense action research is 'scientific'. Furthermore, there is no reason why an action research study might not include the use of some positivist approaches if considered appropriate since, as Checkland stresses, science and systems thinking (which can be considered to make an important contribution to the notion of action research (Clark, 1980, p. 153)), should not be viewed as being mutually exclusive but complementary (Checkland, 1976, p. 127; 1989b, p. 40).

Notwithstanding the claims of commentators such as Clark (1980) who has argued that 'the elements of action research are an explicit set of values, concept and methods that together make up a theory of research and practice' (p. 152), there has been considerable criticism concerning the scientific validity of action research as a method of research (e.g. see Rapoport, 1970; Peters and Robinson, 1984). However, as suggested by Susman and Evered (1978, p. 594), this criticism should be seen in the light of the fact that action research draws upon different epistemological and ontological stances and consequent philosophical viewpoints to those of positivist science but which, nevertheless, using positivist criteria for judgement, can be seen as scientific. Oquist (1978), on the other hand, puts forward the view that action research can best be evaluated not by arguing its philosophical and scientific foundation but by the practical achievement of action researchers to 'develop effective and efficient enough methodologies to produce social knowledge that contributes to human betterment as part of the research process itself' (p. 162).

Table 5.1   Summary of the underlying concepts of positivist empiricism and how they are addressed by action research

Concept of positivist science	Deficiency of concept for some aspects of social inquiry	Action research as a corrective
Positivist concept of 'reality'	Failure to recognize socially constructed reality	Emphasis on understanding real world as it is portrayed through subjective experience
Neutral observer inquirer	Failure to recognize the way the observer influences the domain under investigation	Inquirer's role and motivation recognized and influence in situation investigated; collaborative inquiry
Observation of a designed experiment	Failure to recognize that inquirer brings his or her own interpretation to the investigation	Different views of those involved sought, made explicit, recorded and analysed; recognition of the role of interpretation
'Objects' of inquiry	Failure to recognize that humans are not deterministic but have free-will and consciousness	Concentration on everyday events and happenings as a means of understanding the problem situation; bias, prejudice and assumptions of actors recognized and made explicit
Neutrality of methods	Failure to recognize that choice of methods can influence the results of the investigation	Attention paid to the methods and techniques used and their implications made explicit
Repeatability	Research involving human actors canot be replicated exactly because humans are not deterministic but have self-conscious, self-motivating character	Emphasis placed upon continuous learning through practice/theory cycle
Quantitative measurement	Difficult to quantify all human action; some behaviour can best be described qualitatively	Recognition of the use of qualitative measurements
No allowance for past history	Failure to recognize that organizations develop their own 'culture' as a result of past history of the organization	Theory/practice cycle as means of learning from past history and previous experience
Use of verified models to describe what *is* and predict future behaviour	Difficulty of verifying models relating to human behaviour if we accept human action as non-deterministic	Recognition that models used are only representative of what we perceive to be reality; difficulty of developing useful subjective models and operationalizing them

Concept of positivist science	Deficiency of concept for some aspects of social inquiry	Action research as a corrective
Failure to recognize science as a product of the mind but viewed as what *is*	Imposition of science as a method developed around natural sciences for use in social sciences	Recognition of action research as embodying a particular ontology and epistemology and views of human nature and methodology
Reductionism	Emphasis placed upon parts of a system rather than upon the whole; failure to consider emergent properties	Attempt to understand problem situation as a whole

SUMMARY

The arguments put forward in this chapter have been presented in order to describe action research—a method of conducting inquiry into human activity systems. Table 5.1 is offered as a summary of the way that action research can be seen to address what have been described as problematic areas of positivist science as a framework for inquiry in areas such as those addressed by the ISA.

The widespread use of the action method of research as a framework for inquiry in the social sciences (e.g. Lewin, 1948; Emery and Trist, 1965; Schutz, 1971; Checkland, 1981; Lincoln and Guba, 1984; Wilson, 1984; Checkland and Scholes, 1990), indicates that action research is a practical research methodology or strategy (Peters and Robinson, 1984, p. 118). The theoretical arguments for its corrective aspects to positivist empiricism, outlined above, and the arguments gained from reports of its successful use, led the authors to adopt it as a suitable means of conducting client-led design.

PART II

THE PRACTICE OF CLIENT-LED DESIGN

6

CLIENT-LED DESIGN : THE WAVERLY–RANDALL CASE STUDY

Introduction

In the previous chapters we have put forward the argument that the definition of the organizational information system needs to be approached in a different way to that undertaken in the past. We have advocated that the task for the ISA is to think in terms of 'information systems' rather than 'data-processing' systems. In Chapter 2 we suggested that 'systems' thinking might be an appropriate epistemology for the information systems discipline and described client-led design (CLD) as a five-phase process. This was followed in Chapter 3 by the description of some systems 'tools' and a discussion about how they might be used in the 'problem appreciation' and 'information system definition stages' of information systems development. In Chapter 4 we discussed the practical difficulties of conducting organizational analysis and offered a view of business organizations that seems to be consistent with the philosophy of CLD. In Chapter 5 we continued the discussion of the practical aspects of information systems analysis by offering 'action research' as a suitable basis from which to undertake CLD.

In this chapter an example of the practical use of the five-phase framework for CLD is given by means of a case study. Thinking in terms of an organization as an information system means thinking about not only the operation of its communication and control systems but also about of the character of the organization, or what we call its 'emergent property', and the hierarchical relationship between the notional systems that the clients recognize within *their* organization. The aim of the case study is to provide an illustration of how some of the ideas and the tools that have been presented in previous chapters can be used in CLD.

The case study is based upon an actual consultancy project and is reported in a manner faithful to the way in which the problem situation was addressed. The characters identified are fictional, as is the name of the company and the parent company (which for the purpose of this study are referred to as Waverly–Randall and The Electrical Company (TEC) respectively).

PHASE I (APPRECIATION): THE PROBLEM SITUATION

Waverly–Randall is a medium-sized manufacturing company on the south coast of the United Kingdom. The company manufactures liquid handling equipment (e.g. fuel dispensers for motor vehicles and fuel couplings for aircraft). For the past 60 years Waverly–Randall has enjoyed an international reputation for the manufacture of precision products. During this time management policy has tended towards evolutionary change rather than reactionary change. When Waverly–Randall was taken over by TEC three years ago the company underwent significant and swift changes both to operating procedures and to products. Since the takeover Waverly–Randall has been under constant pressure from headquarters to improve its operating efficiency. The parent company, TEC, has made a significant investment in a computer accounting system which is aimed at exercising financial control for the business as a whole. The management at TEC have encouraged Waverly–Randall to make some investment in information technology (IT), which they have done. The impact of IT upon Waverly–Randall has increased in other ways too as their competitors introduce IT in the control systems used in liquid handling products (e.g. microprocessor controlled garage forecourts). This has had the effect of increasing the pressure on the company to modify its products.

The change in market needs and company policy-making procedures has presented the Waverly–Randall directors with a number of difficulties: they need to implement changes to the style of management and to change products. Consequently, these requirements will generate the need for new skills both in terms of management and in the manufacturing process. Perhaps more importantly, the pressure to introduce new products emphasizes a shift from precision manufacturing into an unfamiliar area of manufacturing incorporating the design and development of electronic control systems. The company could be said to be facing both incremental and paradigmatic change (Benjamin and Levinson, 1993).

A recent visit by a team of auditors from TEC has revealed three major problems: (a) there was significant value of unrequired stock being held in the stores; (b) the company is steadily losing contracts from its regular customers, and (c) the orders from new customers tend to be mainly 'one off', which creates problems for production control. This discovery is particularly embarrassing since the company has, within the past year, spent a significant sum of money on computing equipment which was installed to aid production and stock control.

At a meeting of the board of directors it was agreed that there should be a reappraisal of the company's business and manufacturing activities. There was a feeling that there should be a reappraisal of their commercial activities since this was the part of the company that directly interfaced with the customer and was usually the area with which the customer had first contact. The board agreed that the task should be given to an independent consultant who would work directly with the managing director. There was an unanimous view that, notwithstanding the company's need to improve its operating efficiency, they did not want to call upon the services of a computing consultant. Moreover, there was a weight of opinion that a business consultant may not be appropriate since the board felt that there was a need to re-examine the operating practices of the company and to consider how the use of IT could help to improve efficiency. Consequently, the board decided that the consultant should possess knowledge about business and IT and should be directed to concentrate upon what they considered to be at the root of the problem, namely, the commercial department. The various systems that were relevant to the Waverly–Randall problem situation can be represented in the systems map shown in Figure 6.1.

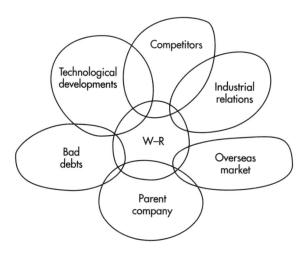

Figure 6.1   Systems map of Waverly–Randall

The commercial department is Waverly–Randall's main contact point with its customers. Customers either contact the department directly or as a result of a visit from one of Waverly–Randall's sales staff. The sales and marketing department is separate from the commercial department, and the after-sales department, although separate, is also part of the commercial department. The commercial department staff deal with all contacts within the UK and from overseas. The systems map in Figure 6.2 illustrates the commercial department's activities.

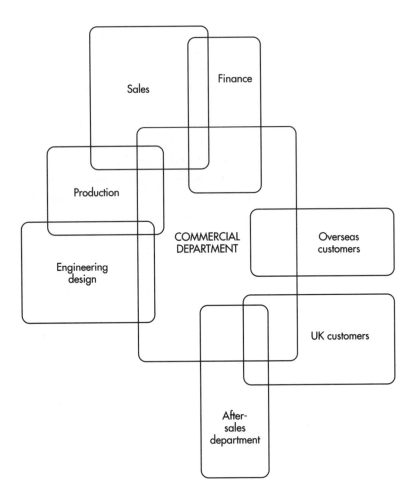

Figure 6.2   Systems map of the commercial department and its relationship with
other departments

In Chapter 2 we suggested how changes in working practices involve changes in day-to-day activities which, in turn, introduce changes to the boundaries of responsibilities of those involved. This was a problem situation at Waverly–Randall, as changes in the market were effectively influencing the activities within the company itself (Figure 6.3).

In addition to the market influences there was a further problem that added to the company's difficulties. At the time of the study there was a dispute over the annual pay award with the manufacturing staff. The pay dispute was linked with the desire of the management to remove trade union demarkation. This has been brought about by the need to change the company's product line to enable the computer-controlled manufacturing equipment to be used more effectively than at present. Clearly, the situation that exists in Waverly–Randall is complex (Figure 6.4), and is one in which an unsympathetic approach to the problems could exacerbate a variety of difficulties.

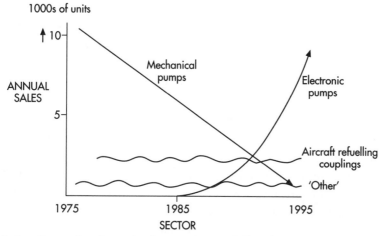

Figure 6.3   Generalized graph of Waverly–Randall and its changing market

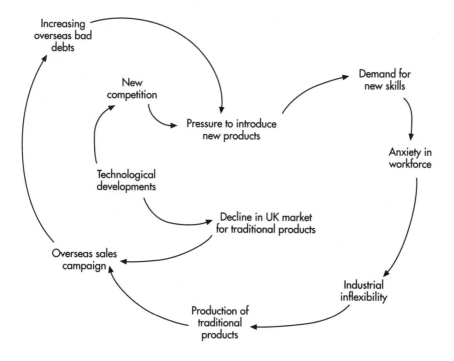

Figure 6.4   Influence diagram showing the various difficulties facing Waverly–Randall

MEMBERS OF STAFF AT WAVERLY–RANDALL

In order to provide some background to the problem and to shed some light on the interrelationships between the different parts of the situation we provide a brief overview, in narrative form, of some of the important actors in the problem. In a 'real' situation the problem investigator would not need to write the details in narrative but could represent the various relationships using one of the methods described in the earlier chapters, e.g. systems map, rich picture, spay diagram or an influence diagram. In the figures in this chapter, we have used the latter diagramming methods to illustrate the way that the relationships described in the narrative could be represented.

The general mood of staff within the company at the time of the study can be described as one of scepticism towards any form of change, but at the same time the staff seemed to be resigned to the fact that change would take place. This attitude seemed to stem from their past experience of attempts to introduce new working practices and from what they saw to be the board of directors' desire to reassure the parent company of their executive abilities to improve the efficiency of the company through changing staff working practices and procedures.

The managing director, aged 49, and was the technical director until appointed managing director in succession to the previous incumbent who was sacked personally by the chairman of the holding company. The managing director had 15 years' service as the technical director with the company before his current appointment. His appointment was made in preference to both the sales and marketing directors who had also been considered for the appointment. Formal organizational control over the managing director is exercised by the parent company through a six-monthly audit of performance figures.

Although the board of directors are the executive authority of the company, the managing director exercises traditional hierarchical power through his position as chief executive. The decision-making process is through the board of directors but in practice any decision stands a greater chance of implementation if it coincides with the wishes of the managing director.

In addition to the 'formal' power held by the managing director by virtue of his position within the company, he also has a charismatic personality, is a persuasive person and a good talker. His personal power can be summarized under two general headings: (a) personality and (b) formal power from position within the company. He adopts the strategy of using loyal employees to support his ideas and has introduced an outside consultant to initiate change, thus creating an impression of activating change while attempting to control this process indirectly. This latter course of action has enabled him to appease the members of his staff who are against change by presenting the consultant as an 'outsider' who needs the agreement of all members of staff for any proposal made and as someone who has no internal influence.

Surprisingly, the managing director has not used his formal power to delay the commercial department project but instead has used his personality and persuasive powers of speech to influence the pace of progress (e.g. he appeared to delay the implementation of the project by continually asking for more detail about aspects of the project on the understanding that this would be the 'final' refinement before approval). It is worth highlighting his approach on this matter since he could have delayed or even stopped the project using his formal position of authority. However, he has chosen not to take this 'traditional' course of action, relying instead upon his personal analytical qualities to find areas in need of clarification while still appearing to give support to the project. The result of this course of action has been to appease both the 'doubters' and the 'supporters' of the project. Those who are in support of the project are frustrated by his actions and those against see it as a breathing space but, in practice, no real harm is being done to the project by his actions.

The sales and marketing director, aged 55, has been employed by the group for his entire career. He was promoted to the position of sales director within Waverly–Randall but, interestingly, was not appointed to the parent company and then seconded to Waverly–Randall which, up to this time, had seemed to be TEC policy for senior staff appointments. During his years of service he has developed a large number of contacts within headquarters and a large number of business contacts; he has also provided the company with most of its major customers over the past decade. He admits to preferring selling products to administration and, consequently, is usually out in 'the field' rather than in the office. He has a pleasing personality and is popular with his staff and with the staff in the commercial department. He sees the sales function as one of selling products and does not seem to understand, or accept, the need to differentiate between the 'marketing' and 'sales' functions. He has successfully resisted attempts to make the 'sales' department into a 'marketing' department and is reluctant to change the way either he or any of his associated departments operate. He boycotted the developments in the commercial department until they reached an advanced stage when the implementation of new working practices seemed inevitable. Some colleagues have labelled him a 'survivor' since he has survived many upheavals within the company during his career.

His personal power relates to (a) his personal popularity, (b) his proven sales record, (c) his formal organizational position, and (d) his contacts and influence at headquarters and within the company. He uses his contacts within the company (e.g. the technical director) and popularity with staff to oppose any changes proposed by the commercial department project. This apparent strategy seemed to reduce pressure from his sales staff who were antagonistic towards the commercial department proposals and have maintained constant pressure on him to oppose the commercial department plan. It may be that he has used his contacts at TEC to bring pressure upon the managing director to consider a number of issues, such as the inventory problem, and thereby divert his interest in the commercial department project, which might explain the 'delaying' tactics of the managing director and the consequent slowing down of the implementation of the commercial department plan.

The works director, aged 41, has been employed by the company for a number of years and as works director for two years. He competed for the post as managing director, but despite his lack of success remained with the company until recently, during which time he was able to work with his competitor, the new MD, quite well. He is considered by most of those who work with him to be ambitious, flamboyant, and one who relishes the formal organizational power of his position. He finds it difficult to delegate responsibility and, consequently, often becomes involved in matters that would have been better left to his staff. The penalty for this management weakness is that he neglects his 'strategic' role as director within the company for one more concerned with operational details. He attempts to control the company through planning activities. He has seized control of all levels of planning to enable him to influence the desired input, sales, to what he decided to produce as an output. His method of controlling production—by trying to 'smooth' the production load by selecting orders that fit the production run—often results in the loss of orders. Needless to say, the relationship between manufacturing and sales is fraught at times. He is a shrewd politician and although not openly disloyal to the managing director has shown some hostility which results in personal confrontations with the managing director, usually provoked by him, and which he invariably loses. The works director utilizes his personal power through (a) his formal position within the company as a director, (b) his quick wit, and (c) his links with strategically important individuals within the company (e.g. the forecasting and planning manager). (N.B. He subsequently resigned from Waverly–Randall to take on a similar post at another company.)

The technical director was considered at one stage to be the 'high-flyer' in the company and was recently made a director in recognition of his potential. Aged 35 he is, in many respects, the archetypal backroom boy. His office resembles a den rather than an executive office. There is no feeling of management or efficiency when the office is entered and despite his executive control over the drawing office and R&D he seems more at home with technical problems than with management decisions. His contributions to discussion documents are often dedicated to grammatical errors or pedantic points of detail rather than the issues themselves. He is currently concerned with ways of improving the metering head for the new line of fuel pumps that the company is developing.

The commercial department manager is an ex–senior army officer, aged 50, who had been employed by the company for one year prior to the start of the study. His managerial policy is one of 'wait and see'. He neither opposes nor endorses the proposed changes to his department and seems most reluctant to become involved in any of the development meetings. He is not popular with his staff which paradoxically, considering his previous career, is considered by many to be due to his lack of leadership qualities. He has a dour personality which does not help his popularity within the department. For some undeclared reason he makes no attempt to consolidate his position or to resist the interference within his department from the sales director. His management style and the power that he employs can be characterized under the following headings: (a) opportunism, (b) remoteness, and (c) previous occupation and its accent upon loyalty and the chain of command. He exercises a lack of understanding about the company and what was expected of him. He does not enjoy the confidence of staff or fellow managers and his management style is inappropriate to this problem situation (e.g. his non-commitment to any of the activities in the department may have contributed to him leaving—his contract was not renewed and he left before the conclusion of the CD study.)

The works manager, who is 52 years old, has been with the company for seven years and is responsible to the works director for production. During his service with the company he has progressed from being production engineer to works manager. The works director was believed to have chastised him on a number of matters about personnel and concerning his functional duties. He is reluctant to include any 'non-manager' on committees relating to studies in which he is involved within the company. He prefers to co-opt members that he considers best able to contribute and over whom he can exercise control. (When the works director resigned he undertook his responsibilities but without director status. The managing director has promised that a directorship would be considered if he performed his duties well, but has privately expressed his dislike for the works manager.)

The materials manager, aged 35, and is responsible to the works manager. He publicly displays loyalty to the works manager but this is seen by some as a miscalculated switch of loyalty as he was formerly a 'favourite' of the managing director and is now often in the position of opposing the managing director through his association with the policies of the works manager. He has been with the company for 12 years and seems conscious of his career potential within the company. He is astute enough to recognize the benefit of being part of a successful conclusion to the company's difficulties.

The purchasing manager has been recently appointed to Waverly–Randall by the parent company and is conscious of his relationship with TEC. He is effective in his job and takes care to make sure that any problems that arise which are not of his making are correctly attributed. He switched his allegiance from the managing director to the works manager when the works manager took over the responsibilities of the works director. At times he appears to support the developments taking place within the company and at other times to oppose them. He is believed to enjoy a close working relationship with some senior managers at TEC.

The finance director/company secretary was appointed to fill a position that had been vacant for nine months. He inherited a number of significant problems, including a number of difficulties with the inventory for which he ultimately takes responsibility. (He was to pay the price of this inherited problem and left the company within a year following his failure to overcome the inventory problems.)

The drawing office manager, a long-serving employee, aged 52, joined the company 15 years ago. He has held many posts within the company and is currently playing the role of general factotum with particular responsibilities for the current projects. He is well respected and has many contacts, at both management and staff level, throughout the company. He has clear ideas on the problems that exist within the company and how these should be addressed. He has also given his full support to the project and the method of approach. He can make decisions, keep them and ensure that others do the same. His method of working is to co-opt people with ideas similar to his own and assist them in taking action rather than do it himself. He seems to recognize his own strengths and weaknesses and uses other people to carry out his wishes. He seems to adopt those who have ideas similar to his own, thus creating a 'pressure group'. Although he relies on his personal judgement to understand a problem, and his action is to nurture the support of others, he rarely takes a leading role, preferring instead to take a 'back seat' and let others (selected by him) take charge. He has a reputation for being reliable and his personality can be described as 'unflappable'. He rarely acts in haste and always with care. He is loyal and can be relied upon to support actions taken. His personal power relates to (a) his abilities as an arbitrator, (b) his organizing abilities, and (c) his personal relationship with staff. He has a long service record with the company as a manager and is valued by the managing director and other senior staff.

The exports contracts controller, aged 35, is a recent appointment following the resignation of the previous manager. From the start of his appointment he has been critical of the way that Waverly–Randall in general, and the commercial department in particular, operate. He has attempted to validate his criticism by reference to his previous experience in his last company. This is a strategy that has neither endeared him to colleagues nor proved to be a successful method of suggesting alternatives to the proposals made by the staff of the commercial department. His criticisms are rarely accompanied by a constructive alternative. As a new manager he seems to want to exploit his power by capitalizing upon what he sees as (a) the rarity of his 'expertise', and (b) his forthright opinions. He attempts to rearrange the situation in order to make himself a valued asset and to put himself forward as the spokesperson for those who have not the courage to speak for themselves. His problem is that his perception of the situation does not coincide with those he considers himself to represent. It appears that he has failed to recognize the culture of his new enterprise. (*N.B.* Significantly, he left the company only three months after taking up the appointment.)

The commercial forecasting/planning manager is an individual who gives the impression of rarely being in control of his allotted tasks. The minutes of the various meetings held by the commercial department project group reveal that he rarely fulfilled the actions allocated to him. He managed the commercial department for a short time before the study but is now in charge of forward planning. The works director exercised administrative control over him and towards the end of the study he was 'absorbed' into the works management department.

The contracts manager has the reputation of being a disciplinarian and manages his section strictly by-the-book. He has plenty of energy and has participated fully in the commercial department study. He has close links with the marketing department in general and the sales director in particular.

The production control manager is a post-graduate from a well-known university who has worked for a multinational motor manufacturer and in the aerospace industry. He is 35 years old and tends to take a theoretical approach to production control, but it is an approach that is not producing satisfactory results. He is under considerable pressure and company rumours suggest that he might be blamed for the inventory problems.

The sales support manager is experienced and well-organized and is within five years of retirement. He shares the control of the sales support section with the service operations manager. The sales support manager manages the 'engineering' aspects of the responsibilities (e.g. visiting customers whose equipment is faulty) and the administration (e.g. spare part ordering). He supports the reorganization of the commercial department and feels that his own section would benefit from changes to the administration. He has expressed concern about the control of the service engineers and also about the amount of stock carried by them in their vans. There would appear to be little stock control exercised over the spare parts carried in the vans and no real check on the way in which the engineers organize their day. Normally the engineers visit Waverly–Randall only when they need to replenish their van stock and their communication with the company is by telephone or by visits in the field from the service operations manager.

The service operations manager spends a large percentage of his time on the road. The sales support manager controls the office administration but not the sales engineers. He has reluctantly participated in the reorganization of the commercial department but expressed reservations about changes to his part of the operation. He feels that his part of the operation should not be reorganized in any way since he and his engineers have built up an important working relationship with the customers and any change to the way in which this interface is handled may have serious consequences.

The senior order clerk, aged 52, has 15 years' service with Waverly–Randall. Although initially hostile to the project she seems to be won over by the way in which the study is conducted (i.e. staff being able to participate fully in the design process). She does not seek to comment on the wider issues of the problem and constrains herself to her own sphere of activities. She is not ambitious but is confident of her position as the senior order clerk within the company and has a reputation for reliability. She does not suffer fools gladly and gives the appearance at times being bemused at the management's preoccupation with changing working practices. As a member of the project development group she is a forceful and positive contributor. Through her long service as a member of the department she has many contacts and enjoys an amicable relationship with the sales department in general and the sales director in particular.

The clerks 'personal' security is reliant upon the value they are perceived to have by the management and their peer group within the enterprise. They are reluctant to exercise any power even though they felt uneasy initially about the changes proposed by the commercial department project. They seem to have decided that they would resist change only as a last resort. Their source of power is their work skills and the influence they have upon the other staff in the department, which is derived from (a) their 'coal-face' knowledge and (b) their willingness to work for the benefit of the company. The manner in which the study is conducted serves to reduce their anxiety about the outcomes of the project.

The sales support controller, at 24 years of age, is the youngest person in the commercial department committee and has been employed by the company for five years. He gives the impression of being keen and anxious to learn about the company. He seems to be aware of his prospects within the company and believes that he has the potential to become a manager. In general terms he is supportive of the commercial department proposals and has made many valuable contributions. He enjoys a close working relationship with the sales support manager and sees himself as an understudy for the job when it becomes vacant.

The computer services manager was appointed after the installation of a new mainframe computer. His first task was to make the computer system operational, set up training schemes for office staff and develop computer support throughout the company. It had not taken him long to recognize that the computer system was inadequate for the existing tasks and without significant enhancement could in no way be considered as the vehicle for a company-wide support system. Aged 41, he had taken the offer of the job, despite recognizing the difficulties, for personal reasons: he had recently undergone a separation from his wife and experienced the break-up of another relationship. The offer of a job with Waverly–Randall some 300 miles from his previous post and the scene of all his personal problems was too good to be refused. In the two years that he has been at Waverly–Randall the computer system has not been reliably operational for any department except salaries and wage processing. Furthermore, the relationship that he had made with a divorcee in the personnel department had foundered and he had confided with a colleague that he was thinking of looking for another appointment. The urgency with which he was doing this seems to have increased with the arrival of the consultant.

The consultant, aged 41 years, is an information systems analyst with both practical and academic credentials in IT and organizational analysis. He was invited into the company to undertake a three-day contract to look into the problems of the commercial department but in fact remained for three years and was heavily involved in a number of projects. The initial study carried out by the consultant suggested that the real problems of Waverly–Randall were not confined to the commercial department and, therefore, a recommendation was made to the board to consider the company as a whole rather than embark upon the study in a piecemeal fashion. This proposal was initially met with scepticism by the board who thought that the proposal had as much to do with the consultant wishing to increasing his contract as with the needs of the problem situation itself. Their decision was to confine the study to the commercial department. However, as the study progressed it became apparent to the board that the problems of the company did, in fact, extend beyond the commercial department and a number of other projects were initiated involving the consultant. Table 6.1

Table 6.1   The interrelationship of projects

Project	Start	Complete
Commercial department	March	18 months
Works study	December	4 months
Loading study	June	7 months

illustrates the interrelationship between the commercial department project and the projects that followed as a result of this initial study.

The relationship between the individuals in the Waverly–Randall problem situation and their spheres of interest are shown in Figures 6.5 and 6.6.

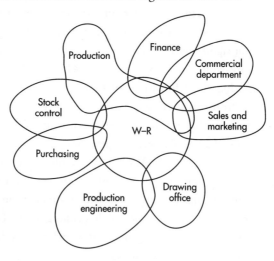

Figure 6.5   Systems map of spheres of interest

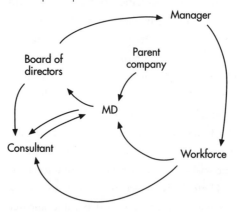

Figure 6.6   Influence diagram showing relationships between those involved in the problem situation

Staff 'for' and 'against' the project (Figure 6.7). Those who seemed to identify with the need for change include: the managing director, the drawing office manager, the senior order clerk★, the computer services manager, the sales support controller, the sales support manager, the contracts manager★, the commercial forecasting/planning manager★, the graduate trainees and the consultant.

Those who appeared to oppose the study include: the sales and marketing director, the export contracts controller, the service operations manager, the senior order clerk★, the contracts manager★, the commercial forecasting/planning manager★ and the production control manager. (The three members marked by an asterisk are examples of the 'divided' loyalties of some of the participants, e.g. the contracts manager will participate throughout the study, but also chooses to remain loyal to the sales department 'objections' to the re-organization.)

It should be noted that several individuals remained on the fence unable to decide what to do. These included the commercial department manager, the technical director and the trade union representatives. In the latter case the TU representatives indicated a tacit approval of developments but a reluctance to formally accept the proposals until their current pay dispute had been resolved.

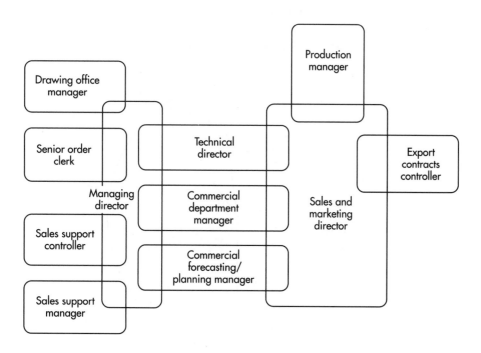

Figure 6.7   Map of staff 'for' and 'against' the project

WAVERLY–RANDALL: OVERVIEW OF THE COMPANY

The company has operated on this site for over 40 years, first as part of a nationwide high-quality manufacturing enterprise specializing in high-quality weights and measurement type of equipment (e.g. scales used in retailing), and then more recently as part of a multinational company which acquired the Waverly–Randall group.

As briefly described above, Waverly–Randall's expertise is in the production of speciality liquid-handling equipment for which they are highly regarded in the market (Figure 6.8). The company's main product line is liquid-handling equipment, including beer pumps and fuel pumps (Figure 6.9). For a number of years the company has enjoyed a predominant market position but with the advent of microelectronics in the control and display of liquid-handling devices the market needs are changing. The processes involved in the manufacture, assembly, and testing of mechanical liquid-handing equipment means that it is now necessary to employ a number of craft specialists and engineers. The manufacturing process itself means a combination of raw materials and bought-out items are required to keep the production line flowing.

One profitable product is aircraft refuelling couplings (Figure 6.10). However, one of the problems with this line is that the orders are not regular and usually the time given by the customer for completion is short. Although profitable, and consequently attractive to the salesforce, aircraft refuelling couplings cause disruption to production because they are invariably required urgently which often means that a production run is halted to accommodate this product.

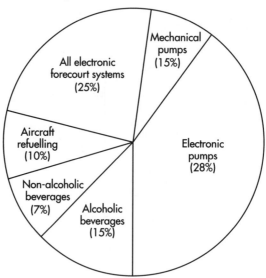

Figure 6.8   Liquid-handling product market

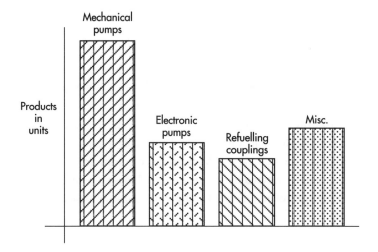

Figure 6.9   Generalized histogram of company products

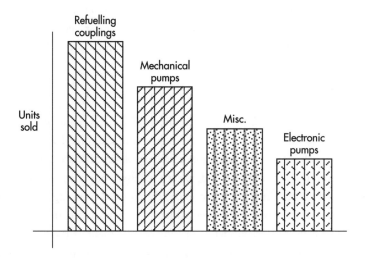

Figure 6.10 Generalized histogram of product profitability

Departmental activities
The manufacturing department
In an attempt to improve manufacturing efficiency the works manager has installed three numerically controlled machines. These machines have given the company the

opportunity to streamline production and reduce the overheads. In order to meet the variety of orders that the company might be asked to satisfy, the company stock a comprehensive range of spare parts and raw materials. Notwithstanding this attempt to anticipate orders, the storeman often has to operate a 'rob-Peter-to-pay-Paul' policy in order to keep the production lines operating. In practice this means a highly complex paper system which tracks where specific stock has been allocated (it is unlikely that anyone other than the storeman could make sense of it). The production controller has requested that the stores area be increased to enable a greater stock to be carried and, hence, improve the company's ability to react quickly to demand. He suggests that the area that will be vacated by the existing machines following the full utilization of the numerically controlled machines will provide sufficient space for the expansion of the stores requested by the production controller.

In an attempt to smooth production flow the works manager has successfully persuaded the board that the forward planning team should come under the direct control of production. The reasons for this are that such control will enable the production control team to regulate the orders to enable them to plan production as a more even process and also to exercise more control over stock. This move is welcomed by the purchasing department, which is also under the management of the works manager, as it will enable the buyer to get the most economical purchasing agreements with suppliers who are anxious to secure contracts which enable them to plan their own production of spares.

The commercial department

For years the commercial department has been effectively controlled by the sales director. This relationship has worked well as far as the salesforce has been concerned. In practice, each salesperson has been able to telephone-in orders which, in turn, have been entered into the forward plan and, where necessary put at the head of the queue to satisfy an anxious customer. Until recently, the forward planning team were under the management of the commercial department which provided the opportunity for the salesforce to have a direct influence on the development of the forward planning into production planning. With the appointment of the commercial department manager the influence of the salesforce on the operation of the commercial department has decreased, although many of the salesforce still operate directly with what they see as 'their' clerk.

Each order clerk over the years has developed a 'personal' data bank of customers, which includes product costs, discount rates, special discount rates for valued customers, bad debts, contact names/addresses/telephone and FAX numbers and contextual details (e.g. dangers from competitors). If a customer requests an order that is unusual, or if an order is received from a new customer, then this detail should be passed to the section manager who will establish a price. In such circumstances the manager discusses the details with production, R&D and finance before going back to the clerk with a costing. This process can take some days to complete and may jeopardize an order. In practice it is not unusual for the clerk, in conjunction with the salesperson, to agree a price and a delivery date without discussion.

The company has a number of bad debts from overseas customers. A decision to stop trading with the countries in question is not easily made as their orders often satisfy the type of production run and skills that the company is currently organized to fulfil. The liquid-handling equipment ordered from these countries is usually for robust mechanical pumps and measuring devices rather than the more sophisticated microprocessor-controlled equipment required by the home market.

The commercial department manager seems to adopt a policy of letting the department find its own way of operating. The result of this policy is that some clerks continue to work directly for their salesperson and some, mainly the new staff, take their work from the manager of the section.

Although the sales support section is part of the commercial department it is effectively independent. All day-to-day activities are organized by the respective manager and liaison with the members of the commercial department is on a personal basis, as required.

Computer services department

This department provides services for the whole of the company. The computer system that is operated is virtually unique to Waverly–Randall and it is only with great difficulty that the manufacturer can be found in the computer manufacturer year book. The computer system was installed initially to process accounts (salaries/wages and customer accounts) and then extended (a) to provide production control with a means of planning production and (b) to produce work cards for issue to the shop floor as a means of controlling the manufacturing process. There are three visual display units (VDUs), one laser printer and a matrix printer in the finance department, and two VDUs and three matrix printers in production planning. More recently, attempts have been made to link production control and stock control, but this has met with little success. There are a number of reasons for this, the most important being the inadequacy of the existing hardware to support the additional processing required and the inability of the software to provide an output that will enable the control of stock. Although each department receives a daily printout upon which the current progress of products is recorded, many of the managers prefer to discover the current state of progress and the level of stock personally before any management meetings are held rather than rely upon receipt of the printout.

The demands made upon the computer system are such that there is a serious problem of data storage. The pressure of work within the computer services department is such that virtually no training has been given to the various office staff who are expected to operate equipment. This problem is compounded by the discontent of staff with the service that the computer system was designed to provide in the first place. The inadequate performance of the computer system has led the manager responsible for forward planning to take unilateral action and purchase a desktop machine to aid him in his task. This example of 'independent computer power' is almost certain to be followed by other managers in the near future. The drawing office is known to have received two desktop machines for trial purposes to aid in the design process. The computer services manager, while recognizing the long-term problems of an un-controlled proliferation of desktop machines, sees the move as lessening the load on his section and, consequently, has done nothing to prevent the idea from spreading throughout the company.

This department is also responsible for liaison with the telephone company for all telephone (including FAX) requirements within the company. At the time of the study there are two FAX machines, one in the finance department and the other in the commercial department. The telephone system was installed ten years ago and all external calls, incoming and outgoing, are routed through the company switch-board. The switchboard is operated by four staff who work on a shift system between the hours of 7 am and 6 pm, Monday to Friday, and 8 am until 12 noon on Saturday. The switchboard is operated after hours by the security staff but this service is only to deflect calls to normal business hours and to provide access to emergency services.

Each department is responsible for the purchase and maintenance of its own duplicat-ing machines. There are believed to be seven such machines, from a variety of suppli-ers, existing in the company at present (e.g. in finance, the commercial department, production control, the drawing office, marketing and sales). The commercial depart-ment has been experimenting with a duplicating machine that will help them with the production of bills of lading required for exports. This has met with limited success because of the difficulties of reproducing the headings required for each of the documents. It is known that the managing director is keen to bring the duplicating needs of the company, which he sees as part of the company-wide information system, under the control of computer services, but as yet this has not happened.

The environment

In recent times many garage forecourts have become microprocessor controlled. The fuel pumps themselves use microprocessor-controlled metering units and each fuel dispenser is linked directly to the cashier's cabin where the driver pays the bill, often using credit or direct debit cards which trigger a deduction from the cardholder's account. The whole process and dispensation of fuel now demands the skills of the computer specialist for its development and control and, thereby, places less emphasis upon the role of the mechanical engineer. As a consequence of this development, the demand for high-quality all-mechanical petrol pumps has declined dramatically. The difficulties experienced from the overseas market provides little reason for optimism since many of the company's overseas customers have proved to be bad debtors.

The parent company is concerned that Waverly–Randall is not reacting to the changing environment and is disturbed that there is no reference to an IT strategy in the company's strategic plan. The managing director of Waverly–Randall has been informed that without an improvement in product performance and in the way that the company is managed, senior managers from TEC will be seconded to Waverly–Randall to 'support' the Waverly–Randall board of directors until the company is judged to be making progress.

The Waverly–Randall management are in the midst of an industrial dispute with the manufacturing workforce over pay. The dispute relates to attempts by management to remove lines of trade demarcation to enable the new numerically controlled machines to be operated by any of the workforce. This move means that several of the manu-facturing workforce will take over other duties within the company (e.g. in stores or the paint section) and others will be required to undertake tasks that cross the boun-dary of experience normally associated with their particular trade. While the union re-presentatives have accepted, in principle, the need to make this transition they are anxious to protect jobs and to assure those members who are to operate the new machines that they will be suitably recompensed for their new responsibilities. There are a number of skilled craftspeople who have been with the company for 25 years or more and, consequently, are at an age when re-employment in a shrinking industry will be difficult. With the incorporation of the new machines and the need to develop expertise in electronics it is difficult to see how the numbers of existing staff and their existing skills can be easily incorporated within the company. The board consider that an agreement with staff to be more flexible in their working practices is essential if the company is to make the transition from high-quality manufacturing to electro-mech-anical products.

The project

The above summaries will be used as source material to illustrate the progress of the Waverly–Randall project through the notional phases of CLD. It cannot be emphasized enough that CLD is not a methodology, but rather an iterative process aimed at increasing client/practitioner awareness of the problem and thus enable the clients to control the development process. The ISA and the clients should be prepared to retrace their steps through the design process where and when they feel that it is necessary. CLD should be treated as neither a series of discrete steps nor a life cycle but as an interpretive framework for initiating a number of activities dedicated to the group as a whole appreciating the problem situation with a view to designing a technology-based information system.

Phase I of the client-led design is the first stage where the analyst and clients become involved with problem appreciation, problem definition and problem analysis. The first part of Phase I, appreciation, is the most important part of any project and is dedicated to all those involved in learning about the problem situation. During this part of Phase I we recommend the extensive use of diagrams since we have found them to help in the process of understanding and, moreover, they can be excellent vehicles for facilitating discussion between interested individuals and groups. The importance of this phase for the clients and the ISA is threefold: first, it helps the analyst and clients to establish a working relationship; second, it helps all of them to appreciate, together, the problem situation as a whole; and, third, it helps the clients to take ownership of the outcomes of the study (Stowell, 1990).

PHASE I: WAVERLY–RANDALL

With the agreement of the board of directors the first step taken within Waverly–Randall was for the ISA to familiarize himself with the company and to get into a position of speaking their language. This was aided through the development of a rich picture (Checkland, 1981) of the problem situation. The development of the rich picture involved the ISA in seeking a number of interviews with most staff within the commercial department and the examination of documents relating to the activities of the department. Naturally this could not be carried out in isolation and was the first step in getting the staff in the department directly involved. The rich picture (Figure. 6.11) served as both a vehicle for discussion and a means of recording the 'essence' of the problem situation. This particular approach was chosen since it was felt necessary to obtain factual and contextual information in initiating the process of problem appreciation.

The next part of the process of appreciation was to present the first draft rich picture to the commercial department as a means of opening discussions with and between

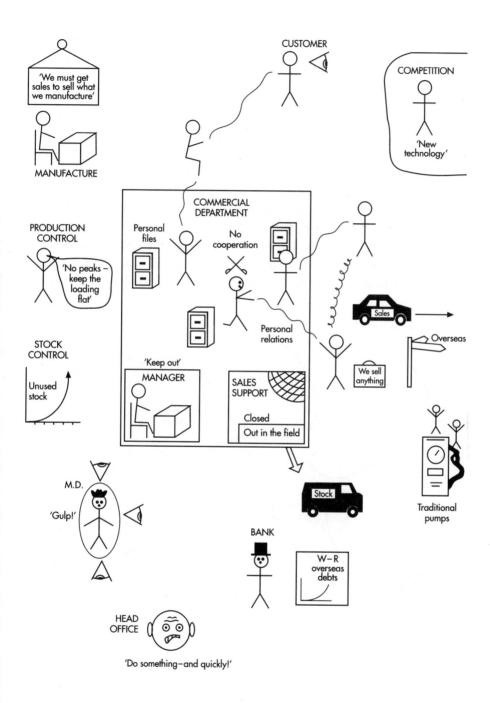

Figure 6.11   Rich picture of the commercial department

members of staff and, hence, begin to increase the clients' awareness about the process of defining an information system. In order to embrace as many views as possible it was necessary to involve the whole of the commercial department. This was achieved through a meeting of the 50 commercial department staff, which was held in the staff dining hall. All members of the department were invited to attend but it was made clear that attendance was on a voluntary basis. In the event, most members of the department did attend, possibly with the expectation of being presented with a completed design. However, it was made clear to them from the outset that the objective of the first meeting was to establish an agreement of the extent of the problems which, *in their opinion*, existed within the commercial department. Using the information gained from the first iteration, the outcome of the meeting was a general agreement about the existing problems and the proposal that another meeting of all staff would be useful. It was further agreed that a smaller team should be set up and meet regularly to develop methods of addressing the perceived problems (Figure 6.12).

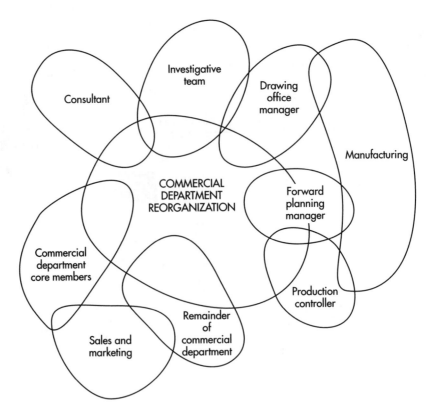

Figure 6.12   Membership of the commercial department 'client' team

In order to facilitate the practice of CLD the team needs to be of a size which includes as many individuals as is sensible for effective operation but also which facilitates as many views about the problem as possible. The team needs to co-opt 'experts' to give advice upon issues that arise but are outside the expertise of the group itself. If possible, the responsibility for convening meetings should be rotated between the members of the group.

In the Waverly–Randall situation departmental members agreed that a weekly meeting of the group would be held and would include eight permanent members (which was a mixture of management and staff on an equal footing), and seven 'floating' members. The latter membership was offered to any member of the department who wished to contribute to the project. All activities of the committee and the time and place of the meetings were communicated in advance to enable attendance by interested parties.

The first task of the committee was to highlight the problem areas that they felt to be of prime importance to the effectiveness of the commercial department. From the list of problems that were accepted as relevant by the staff from the commercial department as a whole, the following were deemed to have the greatest impact upon the operation of the department and, subsequently, formed the basis for further discussion.

(1) Delay in response to customer enquiries
(2) Processing overseas orders
(3) Cost of customer support
(4) Variety of discounts relating to customers and to products
(5) Production planning and fulfilment of orders
(6) Relationship of the commercial department to the marketing and finance departments.

At this stage of CLD it is important that the group have an 'agenda' that will focus their attention upon the problems. The preferred way of achieving this is through the creative use of diagrams rather than a conventional agenda in list form.

The list of problems and their relationship to wider issues can be represented in diagramatic form, as shown in Figure 6.13.

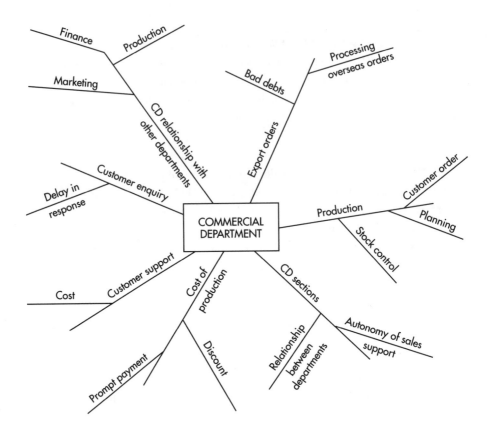

Figure 6.13   Spray diagram of the perceived main problems within the
commercial department

Figure 6.13 provided the basis for the group to discuss the problems existing within
the commercial department. It soon became apparent that the problems were
manifestations of a wider problem, namely, the primary task of the commercial
department itself. The attention of the group then switched from their concentration
upon detail to the overarching issue of the nature of the commercial department
within Waverly–Randall as a whole.

*The role of the ISA at this stage is to facilitate discussions between all members of the group and
to encourage suggestions that take into account the wider issues of the problem as well as specific
difficulties. The objective of this stage is to create a learning environment in which a free discussion of the issues can take place between all participants. It is important that expertise existing
within the group should be capitalized upon to explore the full extent of the problems as they
affect the organization. The primary task of the ISA is to help the group to identify, and then*

follow, fruitful lines of enquiry. This latter task can only be successfully achieved if the ISA views this stage as one in which his or her task is to facilitate the group gaining an appreciation of the problems and the context in which they reside.

In this instance the exploration of the problem situation was undertaken by thinking of the commercial department in terms of a 'transformation' (Figure 6.14).

Uncoordinated customer enquiries; orders support → Transformation → Coordinated customer enquiries; orders and production

Figure 6.14   The transformation identified as representing the main activity of the commercial department

This description was enlarged upon using the notation of a 'black box' to clarify and represent thinking about the purpose of the commercial department and the activities that take place within its boundary. We find it easier if each subsystem is identified and, in turn, is represented as a 'blackbox'. When the task has been completed the subsystems are connected together to form a single system. Nine subsystems were identified in the original commercial department: (a) customer order processing, (b) credit control, (c) quotation, (d) order acknowledgement, (d) invoice preparation, (e) finished stock allocation, (g) warehouse and despatch, (h) forecasting and (i) after sales.

Once a black box representation of the commercial department had been established the group's next task was to define the transformation itself as precisely as possible. For this task the group used the idea of a root definition, as expressed in soft systems methodology. After a number of iterations the final definition for the required transformation was as follows:

A System which processes customer enquiries, accepts orders and translates them into a production plan. The system will provide a back-up service for customers.

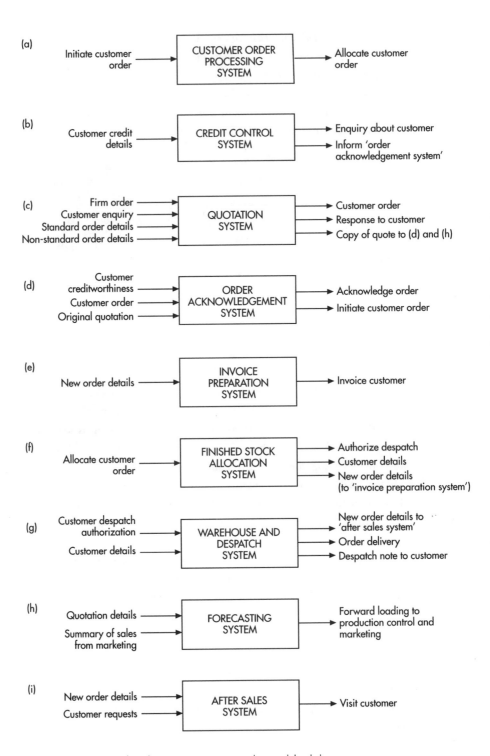

Figure 6.15   Each subsystem represented as a black box

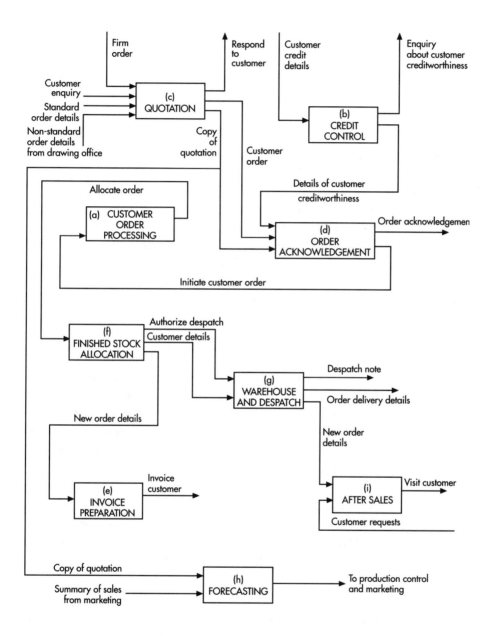

Figure 6.16   A black box representation of the commercial department

Using this definition as a description of the prime task of the commercial department the group then modelled this activity.

*The development of an activity model of the notional system as represented through the transfor-
mation defined by the group is an essential group activity. The process of developing an activity
model from the agreed definition aids the group in taking ownership of the evolving design and is
a means of validating the final model itself. The ISA's role is that of an expert facilitator in
which he or she provides the clients with suitable tools to aid discussion and represent outcomes.*

In the Waverly–Randall study the model used to represent the definition of the commercial department was an activity model of the type used in soft systems methodology and referred to as a 'conceptual model'. It is worth noting that the development
of the model took a number of iterations before an acceptable representation of the
definition was established. The difficulties of getting the group to concentrate on the
development of the model from the definition rather than from a reproduction of
existing methods of working cannot be minimized. An important task for the ISA is to
encourage this concentration and to help the group avoid the production of a hybrid
model comprising a mixture of current working practices and idealized working
practices.

The model in Figure 6.17 contains four subsystems which the group decided could
fulfil the activities identified within the definition. The model was developed by the
group with the help and encouragement of the ISA. The titles were chosen by the
project group and were accepted by them as being subsystems that could be presented
to the members of the department as a basis for further discussion and development.
The model shown in Figure 6.17 is the final model that was produced after discussions
with the members of the commercial department. The changes that were made to the
original model, developed by the project group, were minimal.

The activity model was presented to the commercial department as a whole and
accepted by staff as a viable model of the department. The resultant proposal effectively dissolved the old commercial department and put forward the basis for a new
department.

*The production of an agreed model of the new system represents the 'end' of Phase I. At the end
of this phase the group as a whole, in this case the commercial department staff plus the ISA,
should have gained a shared appreciation of the problem situation and be in a position to express
it in some public way. The example presented above has arrived at this stage through the
exploitation of some aspects of soft systems methodology (Checkland, 1981) and the employment
of other systems concepts and tools. In order to process the development further it is necessary to
show how the proposal can be translated into a form that can represent an information system. In*

the next chapter the project will continue as an example of Phases II and III of the client-led design process.

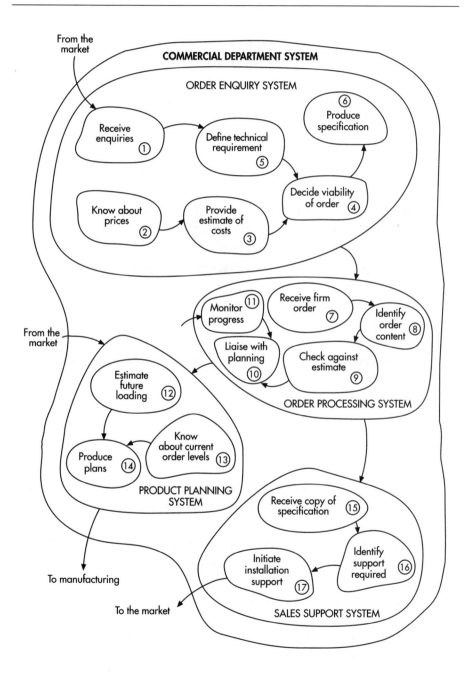

Figure 6.17   An activity model of the 'new' commercial department

REVIEW

The following are offered as key words to aid in the revision of this chapter:

- *Appreciative system*   The power to represent to ourselves situations relevant to our concerns and comparing these situations with standards defining what we should expect them to be (Vickers, 1983, p. 57).
- *Iteration*   Retracing or repeating previous actions to clarify/enrich understanding.
- *Systems thinking*   A particular way of looking at the world based upon the notion of wholeness.
- *Black box*   Concerned with the identification of inputs and outputs of a notional system.
- *Transformation*   Associated with the notion of the black box in that the inputs to a notional system are transformed into discernable outputs.
- *Level of resolution*   Detail of analysis.
- *Rich picture*   A situation in a diagrammatic form that contains a wealth of meaning.
- *Subsystems*   Those parts of a notional system that are considered to make it up. They are related to the level of analysis.
- *Information system*   A notional whole through which the provision, manipulation and use of appropriate data enables decision-making to take place.

EXERCISES

(1) What is the purpose of Phase I of client-led design?

(2) Provide examples of methods that can represent the results of the iteration that takes place between the actors involved in the problem situation.

(3) List what you consider to be (a) the outputs of a public relations (PR) office of a university and (b) the inputs to the same PR office.

(4) Using the list in Exercise 3, identify the subsystems of the PR office.

(5) For each of the named subsystems, identify the inputs and outputs and represent each separately as a black box.

6) Produce a black box representation of the PR office as a whole by using each of the subsystems identified in Exercise 4 and connecting them together. (*NB:* If you have 'mixed currencies' or have developed your inputs/outputs of your subsystems to different levels of resolution, then you will find that you cannot connect them. If this happens you must return to the earlier stages and redevelop your black box.)

7

CLIENT-LED DESIGN: INFORMATION SYSTEM DESCRIPTION AND TECHNICAL SPECIFICATION

INTRODUCTION

In this chapter the Waverly–Randall case study will be developed using the client-led design (CLD) framework to guide the clients and analyst through the Phase II and Phase III design processes. We shall undertake this by developing the W–R activity diagram that was produced, validated and accepted by the members of the commercial department as a whole, and was reproduced in Chapter 6 (Figure 6.16).

In the W–R project the next phase involved the translation of the activity models into another form. The task was to represent the information system proposed by the activity models in a form that allowed the clients to consider and debate the processes shown in the diagram. At this stage the expertise of the information systems analyst (ISA) should assume the role of teacher and suggest methods of representing the 'information system' in a form that the clients are able to follow.

Phase II of CLD is concerned with representing the process of providing the information necessary to support the activities defined in the model resulting from Phase I. **Conceptually, the whole approach is dedicated to the interpretive paradigm and as such it is important that the awareness of the clients and the ISA that has been enabled from the first phase is maintained throughout this phase and all following phases.** *The way in which the information 'flows' are represented in this phase, therefore, must be in a form that can be readily understood by the clients. The level of understanding of the method of representing the information system must be such that the clients can easily continue its development independently from the ISA, and should refere to the ISA only to seek specific advice.*

In this example the method chosen to represent the 'information' flows embodied in the activity models shown in Chapter 6 is based upon the structured systems analysis conventions developed by Gane and Sarson (1979). The reason for choosing this method is that at a superficial level the method appears to map on to activity models quite well. Although the development of a comprehensive structured data flow diagram from an activity model might be problematic for clients without technical expertise, the process of doing it does have some important advantages. The approach chosen—in this instance, a structured diagram—should provide a relatively simple vehicle to enable the clients to translate ideas about information provision into a documentary form which (a) can easily be understood by non-technically experienced clients, (b) will allow a technical specification to be developed from the diagram and (c) shows a relationship between their diagram and all that follows, thus giving them the means of controlling developments. The essential task of the ISA at this stage is to move the project and the clients *imperceptibly* from Phase I to Phase II (Stowell and West, 1992).

The initial task in the W–R study was to produce a draft information flow diagram. This was undertaken by three members of the client group under the supervision of the ISA. The diagram was then copied and used to form the agenda and the basis for a meeting of the whole client group. The purpose of this meeting was fourfold: (i) to continue the clients' involvement in the project, (ii) to jointly develop the information system provision model, (iii) to help with the management of change, (e.g. by increasing the awareness of the group as a whole about the necessary working practices implied by the developing information system), and (iv) as an outcome of this help, to produce a department information flow model that would be owned by the clients.

TRANSLATION AND VALIDATION

The activity model shown in the previous chapter (Figure 6.16) has been broken into its four subsystems for ease of presentation, but in the W–R project the diagram was developed as a whole. In the diagrams that follow, what is shown is the clients' attempt to develop an information flow diagram that would support the activities shown in the Phase I activity diagram. This first draft diagram enabled the group to consider the information system within the context of their environment and then to test it. The 'tests' acted as a means of validating the diagram. These tests varied from specific consideration of the content of data files through to a variety of practical operational problems that individuals had experienced over the years. The problems that the staff brought to the discussions were processed through the diagrammatic model. The exercise served to assist the clients to improve their understanding of the model and, equally as important, of the way in which the commercial department (CD) was to operate. It is important to recognize that while, by now, the clients and the ISA have an appreciation of the overall problem situation they will still be heavily influenced by their own part of the problem. This possibility needs to be borne in mind as the ISA attempts to raise client awareness about the totality of the situation and the relationship of their part within it. An example of the first draft diagram produced by the clients and the ISA from the activity model in Chapter 6 is shown in Figure 7.1.

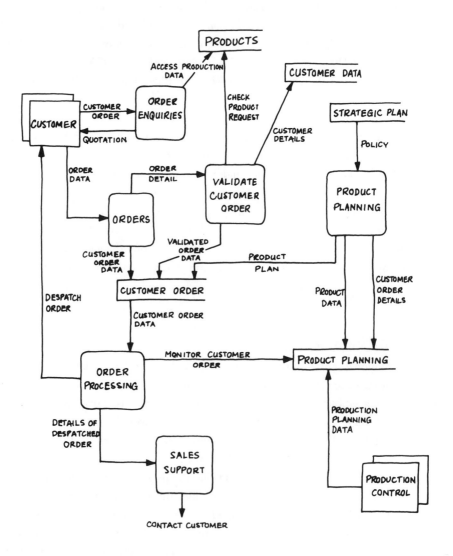

Figure 7.1   First draft information provision diagram—taken from Figure 6.16

You will note that some areas of the diagram are developed further than others e.g. order enquiry system. This 'inbalance' is acceptable at this stage as an important output of this phase of CLD is the process of learning about the problem situation that takes place between participants. The development of the contextual information flow diagram often serves as an agenda to discuss wider issues. In the case of the W–R project the problems raised at the meetings were discussed in terms of the way the department operated and how, in the light of these, the situation might be changed to prevent such problems occurring in the future. One example of the kind of problem that was raised at the meetings was the way that the sales staff liaised with the individual members of the CD. It became clear that some sales staff were by-passing the formal method of working within the CD in favour of personal service from some clerks who were able to provide information to process orders that were outside the normal working procedures. It was revealed at the meetings that some of the clerks had, over the years, developed a personal information system which was not widely available to others within the department. The discussions revealed that new employees, both staff and management, were unaware of the informal methods of working. By working through the model the group were able to see the effect that the operation of such a personal information system had upon the operation of the department and upon the manufacturing plant.

An added benefit of a model being developed by the client group is that issues such as the position of the computer in the enterprise can be discussed. For example, members of a commercial department within an enterprise have an important company role to play in addition to that of negotiating orders, and that is one of customer liaison. Clearly the use of computing can aid in the negotiation process but the personal communication between clerk and the customer should not be jeopardized. Such issues as this are a natural outcome of the model development process.

Once the model had been agreed, the next step in the W–R project was to consider it in terms of the managerial responsibilities that it implied. Figure 7.2 shows how the model was divided into four plausible areas of managerial responsibility, known as: order enquiry system (OES), product planning system (PPS), order-processing system (OPS) and sales support system (SSS). The responsibilities that were implied by the activities within these new sections bore little resemblance to the commercial department structure that existed at the time. The client group agreed, however, that this association of activities seemed to offer the potential of satisfying the information needs of the CD.

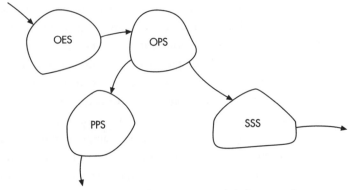

Figure 7.2   The new commercial department model showing the managerial
grouping of responsibilities

This model was then presented to the W–R board of directors who, after a series of
meetings in which clarification of a number of points was sought, accepted it as a
model of the 'new' department. The next step undertaken by the W–R client group
provides another illustration of the benefit of the CLD approach. Following the
acceptance of the departmental model the group then began to define the task that the
model implied. Each new section of the model, e.g. order-processing system, was
considered by a subset of the client group in terms of the tasks that needed to be
undertaken to satisfy the purpose of the cluster of activities that formed that system.
Figure 7.3 indicates how this development evolved.

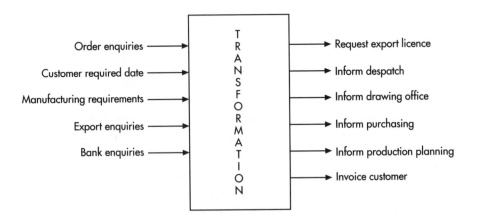

Figure 7.3   The order-processing system as a transformation

CREATING JOB DESCRIPTIONS

Looking at the order–processing system as a transformation enabled the clients to think of the prime purpose of each activity within that set of activities. Arising out of the first iteration of the group the responsibilities associated with this transformation section were identified. In this instance these were considered to be:

(1) Receiving, validating and activating the customer order.
(2) Identifying the material requirements, estimating the resource requirements and identifying what this means in terms of the shop loading.
(3) Process the customer order, organize the transportation of the finished product and initiate the invoice for the customer.

The transformation model was then examined in terms of each of the transformations represented in the model. Each of the transformations was considered in terms of the human activities that this implied and any associated activities. For example, the activities associated with process 1 above, 'receiving, validating and activating the customer order', were described as:

(i)   Receive the customer order
(ii)   Check the technical and production implications of the order
(iii) Check against quotation and query anomalies
(iv)   Initiate a customer credit check
(v)   Decide whether to activate the customer order.

Gradually each of the new sections was described in terms of its purpose and each in terms of the activities that were associated with that purpose. The next full client group meeting at W–R then considered the definition for each section and for each of the responsibilities that were described within those sections. The final outcome of these discussions was an agreed set of definitions that formed the basis of a number of job specifications for each of the sections. Clearly there were some that could be combined with other activities, e.g. (ii) and (iii) above; and in other cases activities were important or large enough to suggest that they would need one person devoted to them on a full-time basis. The next stage of this part of the project was to involve the personnel department, first, in validating, then in accepting these as job descriptions and associating a grade and salary to each. An example of a (fictitious) job proforma is presented in Figure 7.4.

JOB SPECIFICATION
ORDER CLERK
Technical Clerk (Grade B)

Job Description

To receive customer orders from the Order Enquiry Section, assess the technical and manufacturing requirements and validate the order against the original quotation. In the case of difficulties arising from the actions, these to be resolved to the satisfaction of the customer and the company involving, where necessary, the line manager.

Performance will be measured by the following:

1. Order fulfilment within the quotation
2. Efficient use of company resources
3. Timely delivery of order.

Salary: £N p.a.
Annual Holiday and Sickness Benefit: In keeping with company policy as negotiated with relevant staff representatives.

Figure 7.4   Exemplar of job specification

The production of the job descriptions for the activities associated with the transformation identified within the information flow diagram marks the conclusion of the Phase II activities for the Waverly–Randall project. The outcome of this phase will, of course, be determined by the client group itself but we recommend as a minimum that the clients and analyst should achieve:

(1) a mutual appreciation of the information needs of the management decision making system.
(2) a model of the information system which is fully understood and accepted by the clients.
(3) an agreed set of responsibilities which enable the model described in (2) above.
(4) a client agreed method of operating the information system (including, where necessary, an acceptable structural grouping of responsibilities).
(5) an agreed description of the activities associated with the responsibilities identified in the model.

Conclusion of Phase II. *The outcome of this part of the study should result in a clear and agreed definition of the information system. The result of Phase II should go as far as to define each responsibility associated with the 'transformations' identified as part of the requirements. This phase should not be viewed as being a watertight compartment but a phase of the appreciative process itself. Clearly any uncertainties that arise during the activities within this phase should result in a return to the earlier 'finding out' activities in Phase I. In the next phase, Phase III, the ISA will attempt to translate the information system into a technical specification but it is important that any 'unknowns' or 'unclear' aspects of the previous activities should result in a return to the previous phase rather than make assumptions.*

TECHNICAL SPECIFICATION

The information system model is now used as the basis for the technical specification, which is what we have referred to as Phase III in the framework for CLD. The reason why, in this case, we have selected the conventions of the structured method of analysis, as suggested by Gane and Sarson (1979), is that it was clearly possible to continue, after the agreed model of the information system, with the definition of the technological aspect of the development process. It was felt that the conventions used within this methodology, and the way in which they are used, would not present clients with too onerous a task in which to take a leading role. However, there is no reason why another method should not be used, provided the clients are able to control all the technological developments that arise from it, including detailed discussions about the information system, how it should operate, who will use it, how it will be used and what it will be used for.

In Phase III of client-led design the ISA plays a more familiar role. In this phase the ISA will develop the model, with the aid of the clients, into a form that will enable the hardware and software to be specified. It is important that the model that has been used as the basis for defining the information system and the job specification forms the basis of all that follows. This model can be used by the clients to control the outcome.

As was mentioned in Phase II above, the model of the 'information system' serves a variety of purposes and in this phase the clients need to have a clear idea about the nature of the activities that are supported by the information system. Essentially there are six points to consider:

(1) *Which areas of the information system should be left entirely to human communication processes?* Aspects of this question to be considered include activities which involve the importance of face-to-face communication with customers or colleagues,

accuracy, reliability, complexity, the routine nature of the tasks involved, and job satisfaction.

(2) *Which aspects of the information system should be technology supported?* Consideration should include tasks that are purely data-processing or sorting activities and tasks in which speed of processing is important.

(3) *What kind of technology is to be used?* The range and type of technology that might support the information system should be considered, including FAX, telephones, electronic mail, word processors, duplicating machines, desktop/laptop computers, computer-based decision support (e.g. expert systems, multimedia), minis and mainframe computers.

(4) *How will the technology be used?* The group might wish to consider 'quasi-technological' aspects of the information system such as: access to a common source of data (this aspect alone can be contentious among individuals who are used to setting up 'personal' contracts with customers); personal computers vs shared; networked computers; the relationship between technologies, e.g. the computer, the FAX and the telephone; policies on telephone orders vs faxed or letter-supported orders; production of hardcopy material (where letterheads or contractual aspects are significant to the style of document, e.g. bills of lading), noise levels (telephones, printers); and health and safety matters.

(5) *Who will use the technology?* Clients need to be given the opportunity to express their concerns or aspirations about the technological support. It is important that the ISA ensures that the 'power' of the technology is put into context, i.e. that IT has the potential to make improvements but in itself IT is not a miracle cure-all.

(6) *What impact will the technology make upon the operation of the information system?* The clients may have devoted their thoughts to the operation of the information system as a set of clerical activities, and it is appropriate to think about the effect the technology will have on the way individuals undertake their tasks and about the specialist training they might require.

It is our belief that the clients should be allowed to make the final decision about the technological support even if that decision does not embrace the latest technology or, indeed, any technology. We believe that at this stage of the design process all those involved have an appreciation about the problem or opportunity, and decisions will be made within that context. It is the ISA's task to provide an input into this aspect of the decision-making process through a critical review of the technology that might be appropriate to the problem at hand, coupled with an assessment of the benefits within the context of their situation.

In this instance we shall assume that the deliberations will result in some technological support for the information system. In this case the ISA needs to develop a version of the 'information diagram' which reflects the clients' view and use this, once accepted, as the means of developing the technical specification. Figure 7.5 provides an illustration of the way the information system might appear. The first draft diagram in Figure 7.1 has now been developed to the same level of resolution and provides the ISA with a representation of the clients' information system. It is this diagram which forms the basis for the development of the IS specification.

The ISA will then take each aspect of the refined diagram and develop it to a level that will enable the technological design process to take place. This part of the design process can be aided through the employment of relevant technological design tool support. It serves little purpose here to develop a detailed technical specification since we would expect the ISA to employ relevant application generators to carry out the detailed design. However, as a means of illustration we provide a simple development of a part of the W–R information system. In this instance we have chosen to continue with the Gane and Sarson convention, but we emphasize again that any method that can achieve the objectives of Phase III is appropriate to this part of the development process.

The purpose of the 'information flow' diagrams was to provide the client and the ISA with a means of representing their information system and to use this representation to test out the various activities that make up the notional system they have defined. This part of the CLD process requires the ISA to develop these diagrams into a form that will provide the technical specification. The first step is to take the diagrams and develop them further. Clearly the first diagram that the clients helped to produce was a rudimentary logical data flow diagram. (N.B. We believe that it is worth deliberately avoiding the use of technical terms with the clients since such terms may have an undesirable effect upon the clients' perception of what they personally may be able to achieve.) This diagram now needs to be refined in two ways: (a) a diagram should be produced that will allow the technical specification for the computer supported system to be defined, and (b) any other information technology that has been identified by the clients as being useful in supporting their information system should be shown separately. It is, of course, important that the technical development process does not remove the specification from the clients' information requirements.

Although the control of the IS development is in the hands of the clients, the ISA still needs to provide advice about appropriate technology and the effect the technology might have upon the information system itself. CLD does not seek to remove the responsibility of the ISA to ensure the design and implementation of a technology-supported information system. The ISA's task is to be both technical expert and adviser.

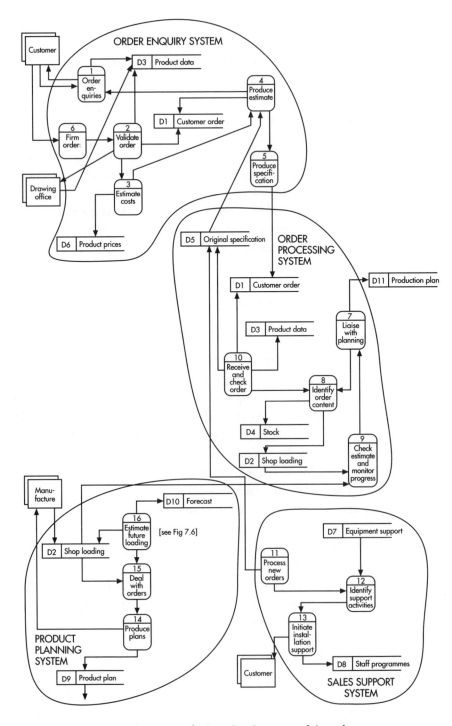

Figure 7.5   Diagram showing a further development of the information provision
diagram

DECISION SUPPORT

In order to make the best use of the technology, the clients need to be given the opportunity to identify the information that is required to support decision-making for the defined information system. In the W–R project this was established by using the activity diagrams, which provided a dynamic model of the activities within the commercial department, and a data flow diagram to show the logical dependencies of these activities. Each of the activities was considered in conjunction with the data flow diagram, which provided an agenda to discuss the sources of information that were accessed to carry out the tasks currently and the type of information that would be required to support the new information system. If we consider activity 12 from the product planning system in Figure 6.16 in Chapter 6 and 16 in the production planning system in Figure 7.5 ('Estimate future loading') this translates into the first draft data flow model as shown in Figure 7.6.

Using both diagrams the clients and the ISA can identify the kind of supporting information that this activity required. For example, in order to produce an updated plan for shop loading the person that was currently responsible for this activity declared that the following information was required:

(1) Annual plan, including reference to resources, unit productions, value, budget.
(2) 6–10 week plan, which would include order and the cost of each order, units/type in more detail.
(3) Specific order information: progress of specific orders currently in production.
(4) Planning information: the current 6–10 week work-in-progress planning information.

Taking each one of the requirements in turn, the clients and the ISA will identify the exact nature of the information that each of these reports should contain in order to support the decision-making associated with this activity. It is helpful to use the activity diagrams and the first draft data flow model as the basis for deciding what information will be used and for what purpose. The procedure aids the clients and the ISA in maintaining a holistic perspective of the decision-taking within the department. Furthermore, details can be discussed within the context of the developing model. For example, the clients and the ISA can decide upon the number of copies and the type of each report required by the department as a whole. At this stage the important achievement is to ensure that the clients are thinking about the information system requirements as a part of a total system. The data specification will follow the definition of the information that will support the decision-making process.

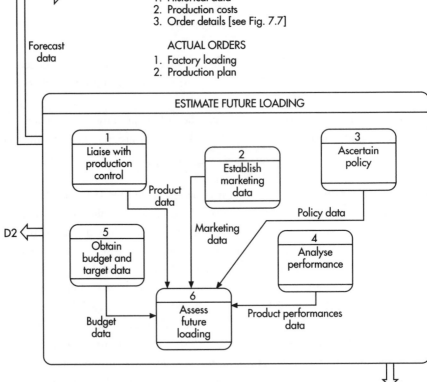

D10: FORECAST

PRODUCTION CONTROL DEPARTMENT
1. Production performance
2. Lead times per product
3. Capacity
4. Maximum and minimum batch levels

MARKETING
1. Market survey data
2. Marketing policy
3. Product sales data

BUDGETS AND TARGETS
1. Company budgets
2. Targets
3. Costs and profitability

POLICY
1. Strategic plan
2. Tactical plan

ORDER PERFORMANCE
1. Historical data
2. Production costs
3. Order details [see Fig. 7.7]

ACTUAL ORDERS
1. Factory loading
2. Production plan

Forecast data

ESTIMATE FUTURE LOADING

1
Liaise with production control

2
Establish marketing data

3
Ascertain policy

Product data

Policy data

D2

5
Obtain budget and target data

Marketing data

4
Analyse performance

6
Assess future loading

Budget data

Product performances data

Figure 7.6. Identifying decision support information

If we continue with the above example, the next stage is to elaborate upon each of the named requirements. For example, if we analyse number 3, 'Specific order information', we discover that the decision taker needs to have quite a lot of information in order to satisfy the responsibility of this named task. It may be useful if the responsibility is explained in full using an appropriate method that will enable the clients to participate in its development. In Figure 7.7 a spray diagram has been used to build the picture of the information requirements. The result of these deliberations could then be simplified and be transferred to an appropriate table such as a 'decision table'.

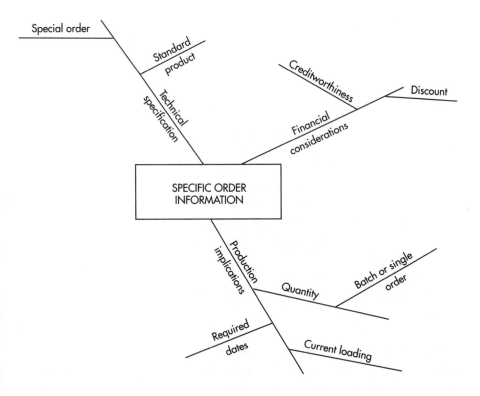

Figure 7.7   Spray diagram of information needs to carry out the activity for 'specific order information'

DATA FLOW MODEL.

Figure 7.8 is an example of the 'information flow' diagram of the order-processing system used in Figure 6.16. above. We begin by reproducing in Figure 7.8 a relevant part of the activity diagram as a precursor to the development of a data flow diagram. Figure 7.8 includes the 'contextual' information gathered from the clients' description of this activity.

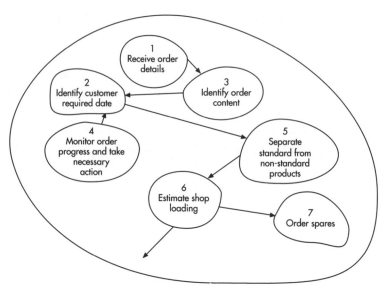

Figure 7.8   Activity diagram of the order-processing system in which the computer and 'other' IT support is shown

At this stage the ISA and the clients can begin to consider, in general terms, the technologies that may be useful to support the developing information system. Clearly there is a variety of configurations and technologies that might be employed, which the ISA may propose to the clients—for example, local area networks, wide area networks, electronic data interchange, FAX, photocopiers, mainframe, mini and desktop computers—but in this example we shall ignore the 'other' IT support and concentrate our efforts on developing a logical data flow diagram. Figure 7.9 shows the order processing system in Figure 7.5 now developed into a logical data flow diagram.

The names that the clients have given to the data flowing along the data flow lines and to the data in the data store are now expanded. The expansion of these is made easier since the ISA and clients have been party to the development process as a whole. However, this activity does serve to highlight the importance of the CLD process since the ISA has now some difficult decisions to make regarding the 'information' that will not (or cannot) be embraced by the developing logical data flow model. The close involvement of the ISA with the clients means that he or she can readily identify the importance of some aspects of the model and suggest how best to achieve the computer support for the activities identified in the information model in Figure 7.1 and, most importantly, discuss with the clients the effect of developing the computer support in one way or another. (N.B. logical data flow diagram refers to the business sense rather than the mathematical sense.)

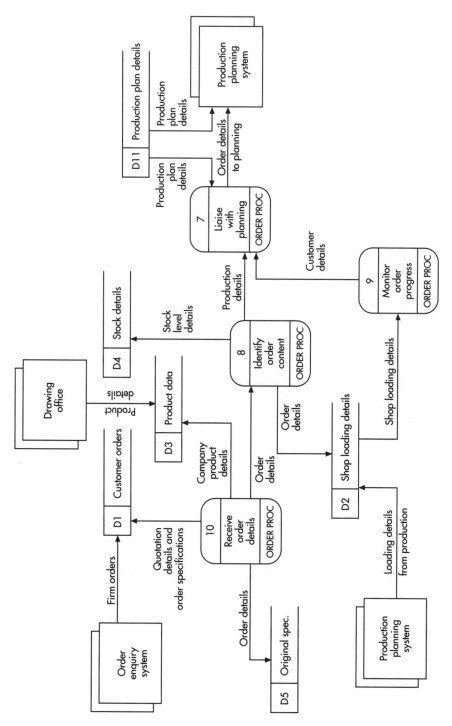

Figure 7.9 Logical data flow diagram of the order-processing system

If we continue with the development of the data flow model as a sort of 'live' process we might take the process 8 in Figure 7.9 'identify order content' (which has evolved out of activity 5 'Separate standard from non-standard products' in Figure 7.8), we can think about the information needs for this particular process. The information need will, of course, be defined by the clients and will include the informal or intrinsic information (Stowell, 1993) that the individual responsible for this task will call upon when making a decision. For example, the client might identify the information needs for process 8 which arise from activities in the activity model at 7.8 to include:

(1) Details of customer order (the specification)
(2) Company product information (what is the range of company products)
(3) Production plan (current production)
(4) Stock level (products available from stock)

The ISA can then consider the input–output listing for the above in which the source output and the destination of each of the identified processes can be identified (see Table 7.1)

Table 7.1   Example of input–output listing derived for process 8 in Figure 7.9

Input to 8	Originates from	Process	Resultant output
Customer order detail (D1)	Order enquiry system	Order specification from [P10]	Shop Loading[D1]
Company product information (D3)	Drawing office	Product range from [P10]	
Production plan (D11)	Product planning system	Current production plan [P7]	
Stock level details	Stock details	Stock availability	

In order to undertake the above the information support might be as given in Table 7.2.

Table 7.2. Potential sources of information/data

Process	Information requirement	Technology based source
Detail of customer order	Customer enquiry details Customer details Credit check Marketing information Customer value	Order enquiry database Customer file Customer credit file plus FAX
Company product	Product listing Report from drawing office (non-standard order) Stockholding Profit potential	Product file FAX, disc, telephone Duplicating machine Stock file
Production plan	Production plan Stock report	Production file Planning file

It is worth noting that some of the information required for the processes named in Table 7.2 can only be partially satisfied from a database. For example, the value of a customer order can be assessed in terms of its profit, but an assessment of the potential worth to the company of helping a major organization in an emergency requires judgement based on experience as well as a financial analysis. Another point to note is that some of the information will be available from a technical source but not necessarily from a database—For example, FAXs sent to and from a drawing office that is remote from the main site.

If we examine each of the data sources indicated in the technology-supported data column we can begin to form a view about the database requirements. For example, we can establish a clear requirement for a variety of needs for the manufacture of a customer order. In conjunction with the clients the detail of the customer requirements can be established; for example:

(1) Customer details, including:
    Customer name and address
    Contact number
    Credit details
    Past history
    Country of origin
(2) Production details, including:
    Product details

Order number

Technical specification

Quantity

Date required

(3) Planning details, including:

Production plan

Shop loading

Stock details

(4) Shop loading, including:

Product details

Material requirements

Section loading

Completion dates

Component value (in hours)

(5) Stock including:

Stores details

Raw materials

Components

Reorder detail

As a function of data flow diagram development we can now think about the out-comes that the decision taker is trying to achieve through the activities shown by (in this case) the activity diagrams. The development of 'Receive order details' is one of the actions which form part of the 'Identify order content' (activity 5) which is shown in the original client/ISA developed diagrams in Chapter 6 and 'Validate customer orders' in Figure 7.1. Through this process the ISA will have a clear picture about what the clients want to achieve and the context in which they operate. For example, it may be technologically possible to produce bills of lading through the use of a microprocessor-driven duplicating machine but the climate, or context, of the company industrial relations may make such a technological improvement undesirable (some companies prefer their own dedicated stationery). The knowledge about the way in which this particular activity is undertaken by the clients and what is accept-able to them will assist in the design and in the identification of appropriate hardware and software.

Clearly, a detailed discussion about the activities involved in performing the process itself is a desirable and necessary part of knowledge acquisition, but the discussions will also yield a considerable amount of information. In order to define the data for computer processing the ISA needs to be able to separate out the external logic of the data from the internal logic of the data—that is to say, information from the data that will support the decision-taking. In order to analyse the internal logic of the clients' explanation of the processes, it might be useful to employ one of the tools identified in Chapter 3 (e.g. decision trees or decision tables). A decision table might help to clarify the decisions that the clients expect to have to make to achieve the activities associated with the process being modelled. Thus, Process 1 in Figure 7.9 'Receive order details'—the above example—which can be shown as a simple listing of comments, might be translated into a decision table, as shown in Figure 7.10.

	1	2	3	4	5	6	7	8
Standard order?	Y	Y	Y	Y	N	N	N	N
Regular customer?	Y	Y	N	N	Y	N	Y	N
Can order be processed?	Y	N	N	Y	Y	Y	N	N
1. Accept order: normal treatment	✓			✓				
2. Reject order			✓					✓
3. Defer to management		✓			✓	✓	✓	

Figure 7.10   Decision table of 'Receive order details' from Figure 7.9

We can translate Figure 7.10 into an alternative form such as Structured English (SE) which maps onto structured programming enabling the translation of the decisions into an 'automatic' form to be precise. It is worth emphasizing that the decisions in this form are out of context and the clients should be aware of this. One problem with SE is a lack of an agreed standard and its relationship to common language; therefore, the translation of, in this instance, a decision table into SE is open to interpretation. It is important that the clients are fully aware of the translation and, when the decision is part of the computer-based support system, are in a position to override the automatic decisions where necessary. One of the dangers of computer output is that the presentation of the material itself seems to take on an 'authority' which the reader assumes to be factual and without error. While this assumption may often be correct it is not always the case and the clients should be made aware that the computer output should be taken as only one part of the information needed to make a decision.

For completeness we provide an example of the translation of some of the decisions arising from the decision table in Figure 7.10. We offer this as one example of a link between the original activity diagram and the technical specification. We do not intend to dwell upon this since we feel that, in most instances, once the ISA has identified the information requirements and validated the data requirements with the clients the remaining activities may be undertaken through the use of application generators.

IF   condition 1

  and IF   condition 3

    THEN action 1

  ELSE action 3

DATA STORES

Once the clients and the ISA have completed the description of the process it is then possible for the ISA to consider the supporting stores of data. The named process and data flow are often supported by a 'store of data', so the next step is to look at the data store and expand them within the context of the processes and the information system as a whole. This exercise is done in two ways: the first is to enable the ISA and clients to agree what is meant by the names given to the store, and the second is to put some structure in the 'content' of the data store. If we continue with the development of the 'Identify order content' from Figure 7.9, we might have the following data structure:

Order data
            Order number
            Customer identification
            Quotation reference
            Order details
            Required date
            Country of origin
            Credit
        Company product data
    Product type
    Product no.

The developed model enables the ISA and clients to consider any associated 'information' that may be required to supplement the data held in this store. For example, the quotation reference might need the technical specification to enable the decision taker to fulfil the responsibility identified in the activity model. If we look at the part of the original activity model concerned with the order enquiry system (OES), Figure 6.16, we can see that in order to process the order the individual needs to have available details of the order resultant upon the customer enquiry which has been checked by the drawing office (DO), a specification produced, a customer credit check carried out and a price and delivery date agreed. This understanding can then be translated into the following diagram:

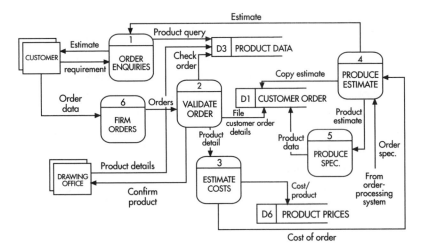

Figure 7.11   Order enquiry system

The level of detail needed to carry out these activities requires knowledge about the intrinsic (informal) information system, and if the ISA is to define and explain each of the data elements and the data flow, he or she needs to understand as much as possible about the task itself. We argue that this can only be gained by the subjective experience of being involved in the study, as will be gained through CLD. For example, at the time of the W–R study the company had some bad debts from overseas customers. On the face of it a policy of not dealing with such customers until the debts had been cleared seemed to be the most sensible, but the sales director, who had a great deal of experience with the country in question, advised against such action as he expected a change of government in the near future. A change of government was expected to bring about a change in policy towards the Western world which, in turn, was expected to attract a great deal of investment and, subsequently, a release of funding. It was expected that the debts would be cleared, followed by a large order. This was important because this country provided one of the few outlets for company products that were no longer attractive to UK companies who were wanting more technically advanced products. The advice given, based upon heuristic judgement, was to continue to trade since it was considered to offer an opportunity to recover the debt and sell products that could not be sold elsewhere.

The development of the logical and physical data flow diagrams is the responsibility of the ISA. Provided the ISA has undertaken the process of information system definition as described within the CLD concept then the involvement of the clients in the actual development of the logical data model is minimal. It cannot be understated, however, that the ISA should confirm the model with the clients at regular intervals throughout its production.

The physical data flow model itself, we suggest, will provide the basis for discussion with the clients when points of clarification or explanation are needed. Clearly, the ISA should ensure that the model is never at a stage of development that cannot be readily understood by the clients. A model that has been developed without client involvement is unlikely to be understood or fully accepted by them. This kind of difficulty may be more acute where computer-aided software engineering (CASE) tools are being used as part of the design process. When additional information is required, we advocate using the data flow diagram instead of introducing other so-called 'fact finding' methods since a new method may act to distance the clients from the design process and leave the analyst with the task of translating the meaning into data representation.

As part of the process of data definition the ISA will also establish the occasions where the clients will require immediate access to the data, where data is to be stored permanently, where it is to be used as part of a series of transactions, and the whole range of data exploitation that the clients may require (see Figure 7.5). The exact requirements should be apparent at the time of their development of the information system. The translation of needs into the requirements specification—the CLD process acts as a means of specifying client requirements—should be a two-way process. On the one hand, the clients will identify their requirements and, on the other, the ISA will indicate how technology may be applied and what the benefits of applying the technology might be.

Organization and rationalization of data

If the clients are given the opportunity to think about the above set of activities and the information system as a whole, then they will recognize that some of the computer-processed data will be used elsewhere in their information system. Consequently, they may wish to give a thought to the best way that the data can be arranged for the information system as a whole. For example, one way is to organize it in an alphabetical sequence, as one finds data arranged in a dictionary. The other aspect is the definition of the data itself, e.g. field, alphanumeric, layout. It is worth pointing out that the explanations that have has enabled the ISA and clients to identify the data might be used as the basis for producing a data encyclopedia, but we defer to other texts for a detailed discussion of this since it is outside our purpose here (see Finkelstein, 1989; Young, 1987).

By looking at the activity diagram and the data flow diagram, the internal and external entities can be identified. This will help to define the contents of the data store. For example, the data contained within the company product data store, D3 Products, could contain the following:

Data Structure/Element

```
RELAYS
TYPE STATIC
    GROUP
            10081/CTCT
            10081/VIT
TYPE MODULAR TRIP
    GROUP
            102040/AVS
            102070/CCT
```

This process, known as 'normalization', has enabled the ISA and the clients to rationalize the data store contents. The process can be taken further by reorganizing any repeating groups of data. The further development of this part of the technical process will take the clients and the ISA beyond the investigation and analysis stage and into design. For all intents and purposes the clients have now progressed sufficiently to monitor further developments against the models developed so far. The clients and the ISA have reached a stage where the design has been specified to a level that will enable the clients to understand and monitor the output of the remainder of the technical design process.

The process of simplification of data stores can be continued through first, second and third normal form. It is conceivable that the clients are capable of participating in the normalization process but this is clearly an area in which the ISA can be expected to undertake the task unaided, except for the occasional iteration with the clients on matters of detail. For this reason we shall halt description of the data development process since the required link between the clients' developed model of the information system and the construction of the data relationships between that model and the data stores has been established.

COMPLETING THE TECHNICAL SPECIFICATION

The development of the remainder of the technical specification will hold little mystery for the ISA since what has to be done now is the familiar calculations associated with the identification of output terminals, input devices, processing times and backing storage. The output requirements are described in terms of the type and number of reports; the input and output tables that we developed with the clients will enable the number of devices and the speed at which they should operate to be discussed with the clients along with the relationship between the defined needs and the role of the clients and machine. The definition of the data stores and the files will provide us with the basis for calculating the processing power of the computer and the architecture of the files themselves. Moreover, because we have developed a specification for the whole information system, we should also be able to identify other supporting technology which may be helpful to the clients. For example, FAX, duplicating machines, telephone systems, scanners, electronic mail, and multimedia.

Once the technical specification has been completed the clients will have an appreciation of the value of the technology in real terms. They should be under no misapprehension about what it can and cannot do or what the role of the technology will be in their information system. At the end of this phase, Phase III, the ISA and the clients should consider training and implementation strategies. In the past, one of the main difficulties confronting the ISA was the transfer of ownership of the new IT-based information system to the clients. It was often at this stage that the clients experienced IT for the first time. We believe that the problem of client ownership is addressed through the use of the CLD framework. Using the framework of CLD the clients should be completely aware of the technological support they are to receive. In the W–R project the clients took full control of the situation again at this stage. Once the detail of the information system had been specified, the client teams began to consider calling for tenders from suppliers (including the provision of associated technologies), implementation strategies, departmental alterations (e.g. section layouts) and training needs.

TRAINING AND IMPLEMENTATION

Phase IV of CLD is the implementation phase. In this phase the ISA and clients will install the new information system that will enhance or, in some cases, replace existing procedures. In order to do this there are a number of actions that need to be achieved between the design phase and the implementation phase. These include training and the clients' agreement to an implementation plan. Clearly the requirements for new knowledge, such as that required to incorporate the technology into the information system, will be apparent as the information system evolves. For this reason, in Phase

IV the ISA and the clients are merely formalizing what has already been identified. The implementation of the changes arising from the revised information system should by this time be 'owned' by the clients. It should not be necessary for the ISA to convince anyone of the advantages or otherwise of the changes. The ISA acts as secretary to the development by ensuring that nothing has been overlooked and by organizing the supporting activities (e.g. training) and overseeing the installation of the technology.

By the time Phase IV had been reached in the W–R project, the ownership of the new commercial department system had been taken on by the CD staff as a whole. The group met to discuss the implementation of the information system and the attendant requirements. In addition to the technology, the group considered the way that the office should now be designed in order to satisfy the new departmental grouping. The sections in the department were to be organized along the lines of the activity diagram, with four main sections (see Figure 7.2). Each of the sections would have its own manager and within the section the activities defined in the activity diagram (Figure 7.8) and its associated process diagram (Figure 7.9) would define the number of staff in each section. (It is worth remembering that this had been partially fulfilled through the production of the job specifications; see Figure 7.4.)

Once the details had been agreed among the group, the next step was to present the final recommendations to the board of directors. After a minor delay following changes to senior management, the new commercial department was implemented. The interesting point about the implementation was that neither the ISA, nor the managing director who had initiated the project, were actually at the company. The ownership of the project had been accepted by the clients, and this is what ensured the implementation.

It is important to remember that moving from one phase to another is not a discrete action. As with all phases of CLD, the move from one set of activities to the next is, as far as the clients are concerned, almost imperceptible. While, for the general control of the project, it is necessary to ensure that certain practical tasks have been completed before moving on to the next phase, the overall development of the project should occur as a whole. It is part of the ISA's task to ensure that the practical elements of the project are managed to a successful conclusion, and to time.

PHASES V AND VI

Once the information system has been implemented it is important that it is monitored and critically evaluated. The measure of performance by which success is gauged should be defined by the group. Assessments will take a variety of forms: some will be of the 'hard' tangible form such as those related to improved productivity, but there will be other, less tangible, outcomes that should also be considered, for example:

- Has the new way of working actually provided job satisfaction for staff?
- Does the customer actually get a better service?
- Is the information system operating as a decision support system or is the technology defining the way in which decisions are made?

We suggest that the clients who are responsible for the design set up a monitoring and control group with a responsibility for the evolution of the information system. In this way changes to working practices should rarely be dramatic and allow for changes to evolve. This approach is in recognition of the environmental changes that will affect the enterprise as a whole from time to time, and staff should be fully informed of the impact of these environmental influences. As far as their particular information system is concerned, their awareness of the effect of the changes in the business environment may provide them with an opportunity to take the control actions necessary to maintain equilibrium.

It is reasonable to assume that the internal information systems within any enterprise will change to cope with the vicissitudes of the wider system and that technology will continue to be developed and be incorporated to improve the operation of the enterprise. Moreover, the recognition of 'information' as a business resource, in the same terms as more physical resources, has become more widely accepted. It is our view that the maintenance and development of the company information system is an on-going process and not one that is considered only when there is a crisis. In Phase VI we suggest that, as a minimum, the client group should monitor the way in which their information system is operating and take appropiate action to modify it if necessary. Some aspects that should form the agenda for the group meetings include:

- training
- measures of performance
- feedback of the effect of the information system upon individuals and upon the operation of the enterprise (internal and external)
- performance of the technology
- added value (in terms of improved performance and the 'resale' of the information available through the information system)
- maintenance
- development
- review of the situation
- enhancement.

SUMMARY

In this chapter we have shown how the activity diagram developed jointly by the clients and the ISA can be translated into a form that will provide the basis of: (a) job descriptions and (b) a technical specification. Although in this text the development of the job specification has been illustrated as a clerical operation, it is possible that this can be achieved as part of an automated process. The information provided by the clients can be extracted by using the automated version of the 'appreciative inquiry method' (West et al., 1994) and this information used to construct an activity model. Alternatively, a job specification can be created from a set of activities identified as part of the design process.

We have deliberately emphasized the development of the information system from the clients' perspective. While the control of the whole process has been clients centred this will be most successful if the ISA can facilitate the process. The guidance of the project from conception to successful implementation relies upon the management skills of the ISA, and this includes many of the traditional skills of project manage-ment. What we are emphasizing is a change of focus for the design of the information system, not the elimination of good management practice. In order to achieve the desired outcome of CLD we argue that the ISAs not only need to increase their skills base but, most importantly, must make the transition in thinking from functionalist to interpretivist.

EXERCISES

(1) What methods of project control do you feel are suitable for the control of a project developed within the CLD framework?

(2) What is meant by 'transfer of ownership'?

(3) Describe the activities you would expect to undertake in (a) Phase V and (b) Phase VI of CLD.

(4) How do the six phases of CLD differ from the traditional 'systems life cycle' associated with computer systems?

(5) Name ten measures of performance that you think suitable for each of the follow-ing cases where there has been an introduction of a technology-supported information system:
(a) a casualty ward of a large hospital
(b) a booking office at a major railway station

(c) an overseas aid department of an international charity

(d) a hotel.

For each case give six tangible and four intangible measures of performance. Vague claims such as 'job satisfaction' or 'improved customer service' should be qualified with a clear example in each case of what is expected to be the improvement in the work environment or to customer service.

8

THE BLACKWOOD CITY LIBRARY CASE STUDY

INTRODUCTION

This chapter is devoted to a case study to provide the reader with the opportunity to put into practice the ideas that have been presented for client-led design (CLD). The case study is divided into three parts, which relate mainly to Phases I and II of the CLD information system process as presented and discussed in this text. The required end-result of the project is a recommendation from the consultants to their 'employer'* regarding their future actions and the reasons to support these recommendations. The recommendations should include reference to the proposed information systems to support the business solution. Following on from these recommendations a detailed specification of the chosen 'solution' should be presented from which the technology required to support the information systems could be developed.

The remainder of the chapter contains the case study material and a suggested set of questions to be undertaken to provide practice at applying the ideas and tools described here. The case study material includes a general description of the scenario, detailed information concerning the business organization in question, contextual information, and a collection of letters expressing a number of different viewpoints about the problem situation. Sufficient information is provided in the material in this chapter to enable an extensive study to be undertaken. However, the case study material presented in this chapter can be enhanced in a number of ways:

- Individuals playing the roles of some of the key actors in the problem situation (e.g. librarian, councillor, student, property developer, community worker).
- Provision of additional material (e.g. current articles on the use of IT in libraries, business).
- Interviews with 'real life' players.

*The term 'employer' is used here to denote the individual or group which has initiated the study, in this case, Blackwood City Library. The term 'clients' is used to refer to all those involved in the problem situation who work as part of the analysis team with the ISA.

Given the size of the case study, it could normally be undertaken by students working in groups of four, and acting in the capacity of consultants. The case study is ideal as an assessed piece of work, in which case at the end of each phase of the study the 'consultants' can be asked to present both a written and a verbal presentation of their findings to their 'employers' and clients.

It is useful if, at the start of the project, the group members take on the responsibility of certain roles. For example, in order to manage the project efficiently we recommend that roles such as editor, chairperson or convenor, quality controller and project manager are allocated.

THE CASE STUDY SCENARIO

The scenario presented in the case study concerns the development of an information technology-supported library system. The library, which is currently funded by the council of a fictitious city, Blackwood, has been informed that it must become economically self-supporting within three years. The change of policy that moves the library from local government support to financial independence has been forced upon the council because central government has made national cut-backs on local government funding. The practical result of the cut-back is that the city council has been forced to prioritize commitments to the local community. Following a heated debate about a number of community resources the Blackwood councillors voted in favour, by a slim majority, to cease financial support of the library. The chief librarian has been informed of the decision and asked to produce a plan that will enable the library to become self-supporting within the three-year period and a profit-making enterprise soon after. It is expected that the employment of information technology will be vital in enabling the library to meet this target. The task for the Information Systems Analysts (ISAs) is to undertake an investigation into the complex problem situation and, as a first stage, make recommendations to their 'employer' and clients about future directions and actions. Due to the inevitability of the need for radical change in the way the library is run, it has been decided that the clients should play a leading role in the investigation and problem-solving process and, hence, is an appropriate scenario for undertaking CLD.

CASE STUDY MATERIAL

The following pages contain letters that were recieved, from various sources, relating to the proposed automation of the Blackwood City Library.

The Elms
Clifford Terrace
Blackwood

10 July

Dear Sir

I am a senior citizen of 72 years of age and from time to time find myself unable to leave the house because of my arthritis. I was very worried, therefore, to read of the proposal to automate the Blackwood public library, as I am sure many other elderly people were.

During the warmer weather I often manage to walk to the library to choose my own books. I find this a pleasant little outing since I can stay there several hours, browsing and chatting with friends over a snack in the cafeteria. I meet many interesting people at the library and the librarians are always so helpful in pointing me to books they think I might enjoy.

If I understand correctly, the new proposal would mean that the public could read books on their own computer at home. Although I can appreciate the benefit of this for many younger people, I feel I must point out the difficulties this would make for people like myself.

To begin with, many elderly people would not be able to afford the necessary equipment and, even if they could, I think the majority would be 'uncomfortable' having to use such complicated technology; I certainly have a problem of not being able to read the screen because of failing eyesight—so many elderly people and those with bad eyesight make use of the large print books at the library.

Finally, I would like to ask how this new method would affect the library service on which so many people depend. It is not only the books themselves but also the opportunity to see and chat with someone which is important to those who are housebound.

I believe one must 'keep up with the times' and yet I feel that this is one area where the old ways are best.

Yours faithfully,

Room 47
Alexandra Hall
Victoria Terrace
Blackwood

1 August

Dear Sir

I am a final year student at Blackwood University. I am studying English literature and consequently spend most of my time in either the University or public library, both of which are excellent. I was extremely interested to hear of the proposal to computerize the public library's books as I think this will have many benefits for students.

One of the most annoying problems I face with my work is not being able to get the book I need. Although I frequently use the reservation service I find that often by the time the recalled books have been returned and I have been notified, I no longer need the books. It is so frustrating but, as I cannot afford to buy all the books I need, I have to put up with it. It will be wonderful to be able to reference any book I need, when I need it. Will there be facilities available by which the user can access books in other libraries? I often need to use the inter-library loan sevice which can take anything from 3 days to 3 months depending upon the demand for the book! Perhaps one day, an international library network will be possible? I am sure most students will use the new system extensively although there is a problem about getting access to a terminal.

It is also a relief when modern technology is used to address the problems of those groups of people who are so often left behind, for example, in my case, arts students. At least this new system will encourage us to use a computer and not to be scared by them because we are not familiar with what they can do.

Yours faithfully,

Redbrook City Library
Redbrook

23 August

Dear Sir

It was with great interest that I read of the proposed plan for the automation of Blackwood City Library. Similar plans have also been discussed for Redbrook Public Library although as yet nothing has been decided. Preliminary discussions have identified a number of problem areas on which I thought perhaps you may be able to advise us.

One of our main concerns is keeping within the boundaries of the Data Protection and Copyright Acts. It seems to us that it will be considerably more difficult to safeguard copyrights and that some form of data coding will be necessary to restrict access to certain publications. A further problem, on the same lines, concerns censorship. I would be grateful if you could send me any details of how you propose to overcome these problems.

An important issue, as far as our staff are concerned, is that of re-training. As professional people, librarians will need to maintain their level of experience within the library service. It appears that an extensive training scheme would be necessary. How do you plan to achieve this to the satisfaction of both your staff and the needs of the new system?

Finally I would be interested to hear how it is proposed to implement the new system since this seems to us to present a major problem.

Yours faithfully

29 King Street
Blackwood

15 July

Dear Sir

I was rather interested to hear of the latest proposals to automate the public library. As a mother of 2 children, aged 6 and 11, I am concerned about the effects of this action upon their education.

My 11 year old son has just started Blackwood Comprehensive School. He is competent using our home computer for games and I expect that using it to read library books will be something of a novelty that he will thoroughly enjoy. What does worry me is that by gradually moving from books to computers children will not develop a sound reading ability. I find it difficult to believe that young children will be content to sit at a terminal to read their favourite stories. Mine seem happy to be curled up in the most unusual positions!! I also envisage some disagreement in my family about who uses the terminal first.

My husband and I have always encouraged our children to read and the house is full of books. I regularly take my children to the library so that they can have the fun of choosing their own books. Both love going and I usually have a job to make them hurry up and select the ones they want. Also, the children's section of the library organizes many social occasions for various age groups of children, such as the Christmas breakfast party usually held on the Saturday morning before Christmas. These occasions are well attended and, in addition to being fun for the children, they can provide a useful meeting place for mothers too. I think the disappearance of such activities would be a great loss which cannot be made up for by the advantage of the proposed computer system.

Yours faithfully

'LynNorm'
1 Wilson Avenue
Little Blackwood

7 July

Dear Chief Librarian

My wife and I were disgusted at the lack of response to our telephone call regarding the apparent introduction of computers. We made several calls to your office yesterday evening at 6pm and were rather surprised, given the circumstances, that you were not there. Your so-called librarians are a most unhelpful and incompetent group of staff which, as a manager myself, I would not tolerate. Had you been at your desk we would have pointed out that the library, as a social service, has a moral right to consider the views of its membership and not assume that all the decisions made within the council chambers meet the approval of the public. We are disgusted at the prospect of a profit-making service being foisted upon the community.

On the positive side I am pleased that you are bringing the library up-to-date—it should have happened years ago as I have frequently pointed out. I have been involved with computers for years and know that they will improve the efficiency of your operations considerably.

I await your immediate reply. I am available 24 hours a day and so there can be no excuse for you not making contact. I must warn you that your inefficiency is the subject of a letter that I am sending to the leader of the council.

Yours faithfully,

Norman Penmann BSc.

'Shangri-la'
20 Ashtree Avenue
Blackwood

9 July

Dear Sir

I was both shocked and disgusted to learn of the proposal to automate Blackwood public library. As chairman of the Blackwood Antiquarian Society, I have taken it upon myself to write to you on behalf of those members of the general public who are not computer fanatics but who prefer the mental exercise of reading a book!

While it may be acceptable to convert technical texts to computer files, it is certainly not acceptable in the case of the classics of European Literature: I, for one, cannot begin to imagine reading Dickens or the Brontës on a computer terminal! Surely those involved must recognize the pleasure and excitement felt by many as they turn the first page of one of the great literary works? The book itself is a symbol of knowledge and learning—a symbol which I hope is not to be replaced by the micro-chip.

I am also curious to know what is to be done with the more precious antiquarian books. Although the reproduction of rare texts may be beneficial in that they will be more easily available for public perusal, I feel that the sense of history surrounding such texts, which is evident in the condition and form of these books, will be totally lost once computerized.

I hope that my comments will move those concerned to acting in a responsible way to safeguard the heritage of the Art of Literature.

Yours faithfully

B.G. Thomas

YFC Blackwood Division
Church Farm
Blackwood

17 October

Dear Sir

On behalf of the Blackwood Division of the Young Farmers Club, I
would like to take the opportunity to congratulate those involved in the
Blackwood Public Library project.

The day-to-day running of modern farms increasingly depends upon the
use of computers, not only for accounts and other administration but
also for such activities as planning crop rotation, monitoring pesticide
control and analysing yield rates. The facility to consult the latest
farming publications including journals, pamphlets and government
reports, directly from the farm office, will prove to be a great asset.

As secretary of the Blackwood YFC, I am proud to present a cheque
for £10,000 to help meet the cost of transferring farming texts to
computer files.

I hope that seminiars on the use of the new system for specific interest
groups, such as farmers, will be organized in due course.

Yours faithfully

A. Clements (Secretary)

Dr P.D. Johnson
The Surgery
10 St Catherine's Road
Blackwood

4 August

Dear Sir

As a local GP, I felt it my duty to bring to the attention of the project committee the possible dangers to the health of the general public using the proposed automated library system.

First and foremost is the danger of eye-strain and ensuing headaches, migraines and sickness which may result after long periods of using a VDU screen. Managers of business departments where computer terminals are used are requested to warn their staff of these side effects and to advise employees to regulate their time working at the screen.

A further health hazard to be aware of is that of back problems as a result of sitting over a keyboard and terminals. When reading books, individuals tend to sit as they feel comfortable which is not possible with a terminal.

Finally, growing concern has been shown as to the possible dangers to pregnant women and their unborn children when using VDUs. Although conclusive scientific evidence is lacking in this area, concern in the USA has been sufficient to cause various organizations to prevent pregnant women from operating VDUs.

I would like to suggest that the committee make available to the general public any relevant reports on the subject of VDUs and the dangers they may present to the user's health and supply each user with the warnings distributed in business organizations.

Yours faithfully

Dr P.D. Johnson

Conservative Association
(Young Businessman Section)
Blackwood

Dear Librarian

Recent newspaper reports suggest that you are considering the introduction of advanced Information Technology in an attempt to reduce stock-holding. If the reports are founded on fact we should like you to consider the following proposal:

(1) That through our consultancy service (CONNED) we carry out a feasibility study of IT applications at a cost of £7,500 (details provided on request).

(2) In the event of the feasibility study being accepted the contract for design be award to 'CONNED'.

(3) 'CONNED' to have first refusal for the purchase of all surplus material.

Our representative will be delighted to discuss matters further should you wish to take up our proposal.

Yours sincerely

J. B. Biggs

Social Club
Blackwood
BW1 2TT

John Hancock Esq.
Chief Librarian
Blackwood Library
Blackwood

Dear John

We were disturbed to learn of the Government's proposals to make all libraries financially self-sufficient within the next 3 years. This, coupled with recent reports in the 'Blackwood Sun' of plans to introduce IT to replace books, prompts this letter of protest.

Whilst we in the group endorse the introduction of suitable technology to improve efficiency we do not support it where it reduces the quality of life. Clearly there are a number of issues that need to be discussed and we intend to urge our Councillor to bring these up at the council meeting next week.

If you would like to discuss the matter further please contact Andrew as soon as possible.

Yours sincerely

William Smith

Alan Grove
Young Liberals Club
Blackwood

John Hancock Esq.
Chief Librarian
Blackwood Library
Blackwood

Dear John

We learn from our colleagues on the NLA of your dilemma. IT or not IT
that is your question! (Ha). Whilst we support the notion of books we
also can see the good sense of introducing IT to cut stock-holding.
Why not keep some books, such as novels, and replace non-fiction
with IT? In that way you get what you want and those of us that enjoy
a good read get what we want.

We wish you good luck with your deliberations and hope that you
can satisfy both masters!

Yours sincerely

A. Grove

National Library Association
Kings Buildings
The Court
Kensington
London

12 April

Dear Chief Librarian

<u>Rationalization of Library Resources</u>

At a recent meeting of the NLA, it was agreed that a dramatic
reallocation of UK library resources was necessary following the
announcement of the Government policy that all libraries should be
financially self-supporting by the year 2000.

It was agreed ideally that each area should specialise in 1 or 2 areas
of knowledge and have access to other specializations via an
electronic communications network.

The Committee requires that you forward, by December of this year,
your outline proposals for your specialism. You should pay particular
attention to the needs and facilities of other libraries and branch
libraries within your area.

Yours sincerely

R.S. Lucas

THE CITY OF BLACKWOOD
BLACKWOOD CITY LIBRARY
Excerpts from past consultants reports (undertaken two years prior to the present study)

1. Blackwood City Library was built in the property boom of the 1970s and architecturally it reflects this era with its flat-roofed, concrete slab construction and large areas of glass. The maintenance costs of the building have steadily increased as the building has aged. Inhabitants complain of inadequate and expensive heating systems, poor insulation, a leaking roof, water penetration through walls and missing or damaged damp-proof membranes. The chief librarian is known to have applied for additional funds for maintenance and repair but this application met with a 'non-committal' reply from the local council. The library site is in the city centre, adjacent to the civic offices. The library building is situated in the south-west corner of the site, the remaining area was used as a city centre car park (with space for approximately 80 cars) until the development of the council's 'no traffic' policy for the city centre. The western side of the site benefits from a line of trees, shrubs and a grass area. Figure 8.1 illustrates the layout of the site.

2. The library serves the city of 950 000 people and outlying areas of a further 375 000 people. There are a number of business enterprises in the area: three light engineering manufacturers, a large multinational insurance company, a ship repair and construction yard, an international book publisher and a large government department dealing with income tax. Each of these concerns is, in some respects, interested in business information services.

3. Within a 25-mile radius there are three colleges of higher education and a major university. Students frequent the library as part of an exchange service in an attempt to rationalize the numbers of expensive non-fiction and reference texts held by each establishment.

4. Blackwood is both an 'academic' city and a holiday resort, which results in considerable seasonal fluctuations as far as the library is concerned. Estimates of (a) student and (b) holiday users of the library facilities are given in the graphs shown in Figure 8.2. The nearby University of Blackwood also accommodates Open University students for summer school during the summer vacation.

5. Blackwood city boasts one of the finest public transport systems in the south of the country. The primary system is the monorail which services outlying districts

at 20-minute intervals from 06.30 during the day, and at one-hourly periods after 20.30. There is a reduced public transport service on Sundays.

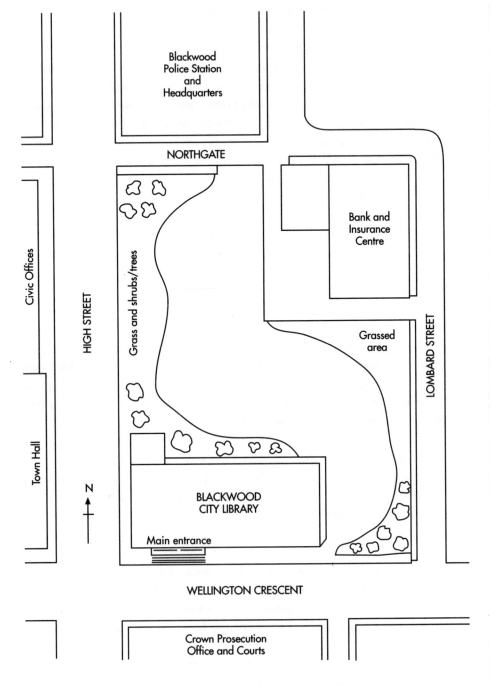

Figure 8.1   The Blackwood City Library site

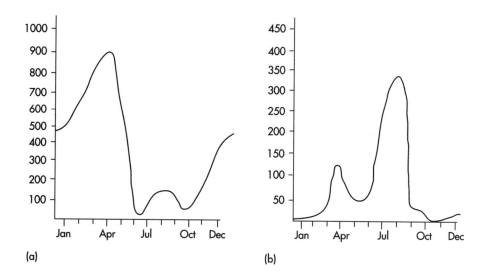

Figure 8.2   (a) Student library users (b) 'Holiday' library users

THE CITY CENTRE

Blackwood city centre is constructed in a precinct style. The library is conveniently located in the city centre adjacent to the town hall, other civic buildings and transportation depots. Over the last four years, a number of large car parks have been developed outside the city centre (a radius of three miles) and the main communication from these into the city are the monorail and the recently installed electric tramcar network. Just over 18 months ago the city centre was declared a pollution-free zone in an experiment to reduce pollution levels and congestion due to traffic. Goods deliveries are still permitted although an attempt is being made to ensure that strict delivery times are adhered to.

Although, on the whole, private transport in this area is on the increase, following an unprecedented rise in the cost of petrol from 2.5 units per litre to 4 units per litre in the last budget, the majority of the population have begun to rely upon public transport for their main means of travel to and from work in the city.

BLACKWOOD UNIVERSITY LIBRARY

The University of Blackwood's Byng Library, which opened in 1977, offers a range of facilities for students and staff. Loans, inter-library loans and photocopying services are provided, and a separate short-loan collection allows ready access to material in heavy demand. Microcomputers and terminals are available for academic use. Specific members of the library staff are available to assist with various subject enquiries. Seminars on the use of specialized sources of information are offered to students at various stages in their courses. An on-line information service is available using a range of European and American systems, and access to Prestel is provided.

Statistics relating to the Byng Library are:

Total number of volumes	37 0000
Total number of journals	42 770
Total area	2 950 m^2
Number of study places	130

Students are also encouraged to use Blackwood City Library, particularly for physical science reference texts.

BLACKWOOD CITY LIBRARY
Staffing
The library staff of 34 full-time equivalent posts and 10 part-time posts includes 16 full-time professional librarians.

Library expenditure
The following statistics refer to the library's expenditure for the previous five years, but do not include salaries:

	Year 5	Year 4	Year 3	Year 2	Year 1
Total expenditure (£)	493 820	535 550	435 620	555 710	545 150

The building
The library consists of three levels. On the ground floor can be found the foyer where library material is issued and returned, an exhibition area, the adult fiction section and the children's library. The second floor comprises a reference room, the adult non-fiction section and reading room. The third floor houses a cafeteria, lecture room and larger conference room, as well as the 'specialist' section (a comprehensive collection of the works of a well-known local nineteenth-century author and the naval history collection). The separate reading and study area on the second floor has 92 study places and 36 'easy' chairs. A further 38 study places and 50 'easy' chairs are available at different places around the library. The basement is used as a store for old and/or rarely requested items.

The cafeteria on the third floor serves hot/cold drinks and snacks. The lecture room (The Green Room) seats 30 and the larger conference room (The Howard Room) 115. Plans for refurbishing and altering the layout of these rooms have been postponed due to the current situation. Overhead projectors and slide projectors are available for each room. Both of these rooms can be hired by the general public and they are also used by local community groups.

The library has facilities for exhibitions, which can be placed either in the foyer and/or reading room. For a larger exhibition (e.g. the annual Final Year Art Exhibition provided by the university's art department) one of the rooms on the third floor can be hired. At present, all available exhibition spaces are fully booked for the next two years. Currently, no charge is made for the use of this facility although if 'sales' are made from articles on exhibit, the library expects to receive a small commission (currently 5 per cent).

The total floor area of the library is 8274 square metres.

Loan stock

Blackwood City Library holds approximately 324 000 volumes, which are broken down into the following categories:

> Adult fiction
> Adult non–fiction
> Reference
> Junior.

The number of volumes (approximate) for each category is as follows:

Adult fiction	46 500
Adult non–fiction	133 500
Reference	121 500
Junior	22 500

The library also receives 440 newspapers/periodicals, of which about 140 are received free of charge. However, not all of these items are put on display but can be obtained by the reader if requested.

Approximately 2700 'foreign language' books are also available, although these books are on a rotation scheme involving Blackwood City Library and eight small town libraries in the county. Readers wishing to borrow these books, but who are not members of one of the nine participating libraries, can request a book list and order up to six books at any one time through a special loan scheme. Books are available in French, German, Spanish, Portuguese, Arabic, Punjabi, Gujerati, Hindi and Chinese.

The library also has approximately 12 800 cassettes/compact discs available for loan. Discs can be borrowed on the same library card as books but a charge of 50p is made for each disc borrowed. The library also has 1418 'spoken word' packs (which are treated as books as far as their issue is concerned), 530 videos (including children's cartoons, popular family films and such subjects as cookery, car maintenance and computer programming). The library also has 214 language packs which are issued in the same manner as books. Videos, however, require a separate issue card and a charge of £1 per video is made.

ENQUIRIES

The total number of enquiries made at Blackwood City Library for the year 1995/6 was 426 000. The breakdown of enquiries was as follows:

Bibliographical (answering readers' enquiries)	66 per cent
Administrative (e.g. new readers joining, machine fault reports, security)	29 per cent
Directional (enquirers directed outside the building)	6 per cent

The number of directional enquiries seems to have been increasing steadily over the last few years. It is felt that this may indicate a change in the direction of the service the library is providing.

TRANSACTIONS

The total annual transactions for the previous year was 1 141 500, as follows:

Adult fiction	526 000	Music	39 000
Adult non-fiction	463 000	Spoken word	9 000
Junior	100 000	Video	4 500

Over the last few years, a decrease has been noticed in the number of adult fiction books borrowed. It has been suggested that this is due to insufficient copies of the most popular books being available and, rather than wait, readers are buying their own copies.

SERVICES

In addition to the loan of books, records, videos, etc., the library provides a number of other public services. One of the librarians is responsible for running the Homebound Readers Service by which volunteers take and collect library books for either disabled or elderly people in the city. The same librarian also supervises the use of the VISTEL set (VISTEL is an information system especially designed for the deaf) and dispenses information to the many self-help and community groups that are connected with the library.

The children's library arranges special events for its members on a regular basis. A part-time librarian is responsible for 'story-telling' on five mornings a week (Monday, Tuesday, Thursday, Friday and Saturday). This activity is free of charge to child members but a small admission charge is usually made for the special events (e.g. Christmas party).

The library also runs 'Matrics' (which superseded Hatrics), a service for industrial and business organizations. Members pay an annual subscription and are then charged each time they use the Matrics Information System. Matrics is an on-line system as members expect quick, reliable and up-to-date information. This keeps membership subscriptions and use charges relatively high. The aim of Matrics is to facilitate the sharing of common information to industry and business organizations. The information most frequently requested concerns currency rates, stock market details, standards, patents and journal articles. Membership of Matrics currently stands at 53 and the following enquiries have been received since the introduction of Matrics four years ago:

	Year 4	Year 3	Year 2	Year 1
Total number of enquiries	9 696	10 974	12 536	12 496

Inter-library loans are relatively small since the library policy is to provide a self-sufficient service.

A mobile library serves the rural areas of the county on a 3-week rota operated from Blackwood City Library. The mobile library (and school's librarian) also serves the 22 schools in the area although, over the last year, the librarian in charge of this service has reported increasing pressures on Blackwood City Library's resources in supplying this service.

There is a noticeboard in the library foyer that can be used by the public either to contact others of similar interest or to exchange skills. No charge is made for the display of notices on the understanding that no charge is made by those advertising skills. A further noticeboard in the foyer announces the special events taking place in the library each week. An example of this noticeboard in a typical week can be seen in Figure 8.3.

The library has five photocopying machines, a fax machine, a PRESTEL set, a teletex and four video recorders and monitors that are available for public use. There are also a limited number of word-processing and text-processing services available.

STAFF REPORT

Blackwood City Library has a staff of 34 full-time staff and 10 part-time staff, the breakdown of which is as follows:

Librarians (full-time):
1 Divisional librarian (chief librarian)
1 Divisional bibliographic librarian
7 Reference librarians (including 1 schools' adviser)
5 Lending librarians
2 Children's librarians

Librarians (part-time):
1 Reference librarian
1 Lending librarian
2 Children's librarians
1 'Ethnic' librarian
1 Social Services librarian

Clerical staff:
1 Administration assistant
1 Assistant administration assistant
9 Clerical staff (full-time)
3 Clerical staff (part-time)

Maintenance, security:
2 Equipment maintenance officers
2 Caretakers
1 Security officer (full-time)
1 Security officer (part-time)
2 Night-watchmen

Monday 7 August

Blackwood Photography Club Exhibition

7–20 August   Exhibition Area

★ ★ ★

11 am: Story Hour—Children's Library

★ ★ ★

6.30-8 pm: Blackwood History Society Lecture

'Cleopatra—A Study from Ancient to Modern Times'

Dr C Gill

The Howard Room .... All Welcome

Admission: Members Free; Non-members £1; Concessions 50p

Tuesday 8 August

11 am: Story Hour—Children's Library

★ ★ ★

6.30–8.30 pm: Adult Learning Class—The Green Room

Thursday 10 August

11 am: Story Hour—Children's Library

★ ★ ★

6.30–8.30 pm: Adult Learning Class—The Green Room

Friday 11 August

11 am: Story Hour—Children's Library

★ ★ ★

6.30–8.30 pm: 'Writing for Pleasure and Money'

Talk given by Mrs Helen Cox

Admission: Free .... The Green Room

Saturday 12 August

11 am: Story Hour—Children's Library

★ ★ ★

10 am–4.30 pm: PATENTS DAY

Seminar sponsored by

The British Library, The Patents Office and Blackwood City Library

The Howard Room ...... All Welcome ...... Tickets in Advance

Admission £4 Concessions £2 Lunch £2.50

Figure 8.3   A typical week of events at Blackwood City Library

The cafeteria, building maintenance and cleaning are all contracted out to private firms. The trees, shrubs and grassy area on the library site are maintained by the council.

SALARIES

All staff are local government officers and are thus paid according to the standard level government scale as illustrated in Table 8.1.

Table 8.1 Library staff job descriptions and saleries

Local government job descriptions	Salary scales (£000s per scales annum)
Professional librarians	
Principal librarian	30.00–36.50
Librarian	22.00–27.00
Assistant librarian	15.25–19.50
Administrative officers	
Senior administrator	23.50–28.00
Administrator	20.00–24.25
Assistant administrator	16.50–19.50
Clerical officer	15.80–17.50
Clerical assistant	14.50–16.00
Catering staff	
Catering manager	15.80–20.00
Catering assistant	12.50–15.00
Maintenance staff	
Senior maintenance engineer	16.50–19.75
Maintenance engineer	13.50–17.50
Non-technical staff	
Security officer	14.00–15.75
*Information systems analyst**	
Senior information systems analyst	25.50–28.75
Information systems analyst	22.50–26.00
Assistant information systems analyst	18.75–21.00
Senior programmer	17.50–23.00
Programmer	15.25–18.75

*Equate consultants' salaries with ISAs'

SUMMARY OF FACILITIES

Item issue/return database which also serves the data-processing needs of the library, including:

Stock interrogation system (for public use)

Stock control

Word processing

Reports (e.g. overdue item reminders).

The library uses a popular spreadsheet package for its accounting procedures (choice of this package was directed by local government policy in an attempt to ensure compatibility across its offices). The library also houses a computer-based Expert System for Social Security Benefits Advice (needs updating).

Equipment

VAX 11/750 with 6 Mbyte of main memory and 456 Mbyte of backing storage; 30 terminal lines for various peripheral equipment.

Network PCs with 40 Mbyte fileservers 16 terminals

5 Microfiche terminals

Video recorder with large TV screen monitor

Voice-activated equipment for use with PCs

5 Photocopying machines

1 Compact disc player

3 CD-ROM machines on PCs.

CASE STUDY PROJECT

The project specification is divided into three parts, with each part having its own set of objectives and outcomes. However, although the three parts have been developed as a means of dividing the overall project into manageable sections, together they do form a complete whole.

TASK OUTLINE

You are a member of a small group of consultants engaged by Blackwood City Library (your 'employers') to investigate the feasibility of enabling the library to become a self-funded enterprise within three years of the present date. An important factor in achieving this objective is expected to be the skilful and innovative use of a variety of appropriate information technologies. A recent study carried out by a software house into the feasibility of replacing the existing public library computer systems with a new computer-based information system made proposals that were unpopular and too limited, given the range of technologies that are currently available. Furthermore, at the time of the previous study the recent decision by the council to cease funding the library in three years' time had not been known.

The three stages of the project are as follows:

(1) Phase I is concerned with problem appreciation and definition.
(2) Phase II is concerned with problem analysis and formalization (in terms of two potential 'solutions' to the problem situation).
(3) Phase III is concerned with the development of the chosen 'solution'. This includes the definition of any identified information system and job specifications to support the proposed 'solution'.

It is possible to extend the project as far as a technical specification including the production, where applicable, of specific software, or the use of a particular package (e.g. database or hypertext information retrieval system).

Wherever possible the consultants should supplement the case study material provided here with research into the way in which libraries operate, the problems they are facing, and the role that IT is playing now and might play in the future.

If role-playing is to be used in the study, then the characters that may be involved include the chief librarian, a local councillor, a health and safety officer, a student representative, a property developer and a community worker. The number of 'live' role players in the exercise should be clearly stated by the project supervisor at the start of the study. The role-players themselves will provide a 'timetable' of interviews at which they will be available to answer your group's questions. The role-playing exercise should be conducted formally with appointments for interview made in advance and the interviews themselves should be undertaken in a professional manner with the role-players being treated as 'real world' clients. As is often the case in 'real world' situations, you might find that your appointment is cancelled at the last moment and without prior warning. In such circumstances you should arrange another appointment. Try to anticipate such eventualities in your project plan so that the project will not be too disrupted.

TASK: PHASE I

(Suggested weighting for assessment purposes for Phase I is 35 per cent; 70 per cent of this mark is for the written submission and 30 per cent for the verbal presentation.)

Project objectives

The first phase of the project is intended to provide each member of the consultancy group with experience of the following activities:

(1) Problem appreciation and description (Phase I of CLD). In CLD this process should also be experienced by the clients

(2) Contributing and working effectively as part of a team

(3) Developing and demonstrating communication skills (through the production of a written report followed by a verbal presentation of the report)

(4) Working with clients to develop an appreciation of the situation in all those involved in the scenario

(5) The development of project planning and control skills (through the satisfactory and timely completion of tasks).

This part of the study is concerned with Phase I of CLD. You may find it difficult to restrict yourself to problem-appreciation and problem-definition but it is essential that you do. Avoid being tempted to try to solve 'the problem' and concentrate upon understanding fully the complexity of the situation under investigation.

As a guideline, in this first part of the project you will need to consider the following points:

(1) What is the nature of the organization under investigation and what services does it provide? How are these services related and what data do they share?

(2) What is the context of the present investigation and how is the investigation likely to be received by those within the problem situation?

(3) What information systems can be identified within the organization?

(4) What information technology is currently used? How is this IT used and how effective is it?

(5) How do the human communication systems and technology-supported information systems interact? What effect does the current technology-supported information system have upon the human communication systems and upon the way in which the organization operates?

(6) What are the implications of 'wider' information systems upon the organizational information systems?

(7) How do the various departments or subsystems within the organization interact?

(8) Who are the main actors in the problem situation and what are their roles? How do they interact and communicate?

(9) How can the many dimensions of the problem situation, represented by the above questions, be illustrated and represented?

(10) How can you make sure that your clients are fully involved in this phase of the investigation? How can you be sure that you have fully understood what you have been told by those involved in the situation?

For this phase of the project your group should produce a printed report (as a rough guide you should be looking to produce about 20 sides of A4) in which the problem situation is presented. The report should make full use of appropriate diagrams and each diagram used should be accompanied by a brief discussion of salient features of the problem situation that this diagram represents. The reasons for choosing the particular diagram should also be included (some useful diagrams for this stage of the project can be found in Chapters 2 and 3). As a minimum, you should ensure that each of the ten points identified above has been addressed within your report.

The report should include a description of the way in which the clients have been involved in the study. It is not necessary that the view of your 'employer' should coincide with the view of your group at all times. It is the identification of areas of disagreement between the perspective of 'employer' and consultant that fuels the appreciative process in that through discussion of these points a richer understanding of the problem situation is reached. What is important is that any disagreement should not halt the project. Should any serious disagreement evolve, the report should document the different positions and describe the group's intended action to resolve the conflict.

Following the submission of the printed report the group will make a formal verbal presentation to their 'employer' and clients. All members of the group must participate. Questions will be directed at individual members of the consultancy group, which should be answered in a professional manner. Remember the quality of the final submission is the group's responsibility and marks will be awarded upon critical examination of the report.

TASK: PHASE II
(Suggested weighting for assessment purposes for Phase II is 35 per cent; 70 per cent of this mark is for the written submission and 30 per cent for the verbal presentation.)

Project objectives
The second phase of the project is intended to provide each member of the consultancy group with experience of the following activities:

(1) The selection of appropriate methods of problem representation suited for this particular problem situation and for the clients (Chapters 2, 3 and 4 will assist here)
(2) The process of problem analysis and formulation in a situation including both quantitative and qualitative elements

(3) The production of at least two potential ways of addressing the identified problem situation

(4) Working with clients to produce a thorough description of the problem situation and two potential ways forward

(5) Working within a group to produce a comprehensive document within a defined time-scale.

In this phase of the project you should use the material and the appreciation that you have gained during Phase I about the problem situation to analyse the problem. Do not hesitate to review what you learned in Phase I in the light of what you discover as you carry out the analysis. For example, you might decide that you need more information about a particular aspect of the problem. It is important to remember that at this stage you are not attempting to detail a solution but to identify what appear to you and your clients to be the key problem areas. Arising from this description you will produce at least two potential ways of addressing the problems highlighted. Your clients should play a dominant role in helping with the analysis and in validating your work.

There are, as you have no doubt discovered in Phase I, a number of views about the nature of the problem. There are the views of the librarian, the councillor, and those of the business community and local community which, at times, may seem to be at variance. What you should now do is try to represent these views in a way that will help show the situation that you perceive and then analyse the result of your effort (Chapters 2 and 3 will help here). For example, it might be useful if you were to produce an influence diagram which represents the views of the main characters in the situation. You could complement this with a detailed black box diagram of the situation as it is at present. What you will have represented is some of the functional and contextual aspects of the situation. Once you have represented the problem situation in this relatively unbiased way, you might then be in a position to begin your analysis. It is advisable at this stage of the project to get at least two clear definitions of the problem (which should be discussed in the narrative part of your report) and ways in which each might be addressed (i.e. two potential 'solutions'). For example, it may be worth while seeking the opinions of the librarian and the councillor as they represent, as far as this project is concerned, differing views about the value of Blackwood City Library. Reference should be made to the impact that you feel each of the views might have upon the outcome were they to prevail. Your consultancy group should identify the ramifications of the decision to make the library self-supporting and the options that may be open to the librarian. Your analysis should include a first attempt at assessing the likely benefits and disadvantages of each 'solution'. On a practical note, do not overlook who has employed you—do you think this will influence your decision?

There is no doubt that IT will play an important role in your final recommendations but you should remember that there are a variety of technologies that might be employed. Do not limit your thinking to computers but consider the way in which IT might be utilized to underpin the type of 'information system' that the library as a whole may represent. A successful outcome of the project will rely as much upon the relationship that you develop with your clients and your group's understanding of the problem as upon your creative use of technology.

Your final task in this phase is to state which of the two possible ways forward your group favours and why. In this part of the project the following specific points should be considered by your group:

(1) The relationship of the principal actors in the situation and the influence their opinions could have upon the way in which the project developed.
(2) The wider human communication systems that make up the library system as a whole (e.g. business/private), showing how they were discovered and detailing the tools that were used to represent this complex domain. Explain why these tools were selected and how they were used in your analysis.
(3) How you identified and represented the 'typical' organizational structures to be found within the library system (as a whole) including: consideration of 'typical' lines of responsibility; definition of organizational functions; inter- and intra-departmental responsibilities; the effect of IT upon the organizational structure; the way in which the organization's objectives are defined.
(4) The means by which information systems contribute to the achievement of the goals and objectives of the study as defined by your 'employer'. Consideration should be given to: the need for and value of IT within organizational information systems; motivational factors that are believed to enhance employee effectiveness; methods of establishing the degree of attainment of goals and objectives; the impact of the current IT system upon employees and customers.
(5) The likely effect upon the community if the library does/does not become self-supporting. A brief summary of the effects a profit-making library will have upon the working practices of the library employees.

This second part of the project requires the group to provide a written report which, as in Phase I, comprises identifiable sections by each member. Clearly, there will be an editing function as the report must be coherent and be seen by your 'employer' as one report but with identified sections for which each member has a clear responsibility. The report should contain annexes which provide supporting material for the analysis contained within the body of the report (e.g. printouts of the spreadsheets used for the analysis of the statistics contained within the case study material). As a rough guide, each section of the report should be a minimum of five sides of A4, excluding the contents page and annexes. To conclude this phase of the study your group will give a verbal presentation to an informed audience in which each member of the group will present the results of his or her part of the analysis.

TASK: PHASE III

(Suggested weighting for assessment purposes for Phase III is 30 per cent; 50 per cent of this mark is for the written submission and 50 per cent for the verbal presentation.)

Project objectives

The third, and final, phase of the project is intended to provide each member of the consultancy group with experience of the following activities:

(1) The production and presentation of a set of recommendations to an informed audience
(2) Working as part of a team to produce a cohesive, quality document within a predefined time-scale
(3) The production of a set of recommendations, validated by clients (e.g. by means of written confirmation), relating to the application of technology to support the activities of the business enterprise.

Phase III combines the results of the previous two phases into a detailed report in which you make recommendations to your 'employer' and clients about the future direction of the library and the IT that will support the future library information system(s). Even at this late stage in the project, do not be afraid of revisiting ground previously covered. The ideas and recommendations made by your group may well initiate further discussion with those involved in the situation which, in turn, may necessitate further fact-finding and analysis.

In this final phase of the project, you should prepare a written report which capitalizes on the work carried out in Phases I and II. You should describe the overall problem situation, taking care to include both contextual and factual elements (e.g. the information acquired during Phase I). The report should continue with a short discussion of the main areas for concern that you perceive as existing in the problem situation (e.g. the result of your analysis at Phase II). You need to state the 'problems', or areas of concern, that you feel need to be tackled first, and explain why. Your analysis needs to state clearly whether the considered problem seems to be at the root of the matter or whether it is a manifestation of a deeper problem which, for good reason, you feel cannot be addressed at this time. You should also include written confirmation that your recommendation has been approved by your 'employer'.

Your report needs to include a suitable diagram depicting the library's information system as a whole. This representation needs to be developed further to indicate the areas in which IT might support the associated activities. You should select two tasks from within this web of activities and provide a job description for each of them. You should then give an example of the technology that might be used by the person who will fulfil the task description.

In this phase of the study your group should ensure that the following are included in the report:

(1) Recommendations to the 'employer' and clients about the future development of the library
(2) Recommendations concerning the use of appropriate information technology
(3) A discussion of the changes to working practices and organizational operations incumbent upon the group's recommendations.

By the end of Phase II you should have made two recommendations to your 'employer' and clients, one of which you will have put forward as your favoured option (complete with supporting evidence). In Phase III you will take your favoured option and develop it further to include:

(i) a structured diagram (use the Gane and Sarson model shown in your notes) of the recommended information system;
(ii) a systems map of the new library system and its environment (i.e. the main users of the new library);
(iii) estimated income and expenditure over a 5-year period starting from one year before the date on which the library becomes self-supporting.

The spreadsheet for (iii) above should include estimated cost of equipment, salaries, buildings costs, publications and income from business, the community (e.g. from the council for services) and rental/sale of any 'free' space. The information in the spreadsheet should be presented by means of charts, histograms and graphs where appropriate.

In this final phase, the group's work will be assessed in terms of the soundness of the proposals (and the evidence that supports them), the coherence of the report as a whole and the quality of material. A verbal presentation of the final report will also take place.

END NOTE

We have attempted to provide within this text some ideas that may assist the modern information systems professional in addressing the problem of developing technology supported information systems. The well-publicized computer system failures of the 1990s—e.g. The London Ambulance System, the Stock Exchange, the Performing Rights computer system and the Police information system—seem to be related as much to the management and development of the technology as to the technical design itself. The reasons for the failures are varied, but one important feature that seems to be common is that most of the failures owe as much to the difference between client expectation and reality as anything else. This is obvious you might say, because that is what a failure is, but that simplicity lies at the heart of the problem. Clients and analyst are often talking a different language; what the analyst means by information is not always what the clients understand, and what the clients mean by computer performance is often at variance with the performance that the technically minded analyst has in mind. The 'models' to which each is relating are very different and this, we suggest, is partially the reason why expectations are rarely matched by the outcome.

Increasingly the net effect of the installation of computer systems has resulted in a bad press. We have argued that advances in technology have made the computer itself 'transparent' to its user and hence the analyst should be concerned, as a first priority, with defining the information system followed by a definition of the technology that can support the information system. The focus of attention is then upon appreciating the information that is required to enable a given set of activities to take place. Embedded within such a requirement is the need to identify the tasks with respect to the perceived purpose of the enterprise. The ISA's objective is to help to establish these tasks, to appreciate them, and to enable the clients to appreciate them. We have proposed that the methods of analysis that are traditionally associated with computer system definition are inappropriate for the task of appreciation and information system definition. Most of the tools available to the analyst, we have suggested, were developed for a clear technical end and are not appropriate for the initial phase of the investigation, which we have referred to as Phase I. In recognition of this deficiency a number of approaches have been developed and some analysts have changed their style of investigation in an attempt to address the difficult task of analysis, design and implementation.

We suggest that what is required is an evaluation of the roles and educational process of the analysis and design process as a whole. The real failure, it seems, is the absence of a discipline of information systems. In a world in which technology plays such an important part, and in which the technological applications are developing at a phenomenal rate, a sound intellectual basis from which to develop the practice seems to be essential. The education and training received by the would-be ISA should no longer be a subset of computing science but a distinct area of learning. We have suggested that the modern analyst needs technical and analytical skills and we have offered the systems epistemology as the intellectual underpinning of the profession. We are under no illusions that what we have presented in this little book is the answer to the complexities of modern information systems development. We have attempted to represent a concept, together with a number of potentially useful tools that the ISA might find useful. These tools, we have suggested, can link in to some of the ideas in current use and to some in development (e.g. OOA). We have stressed the importance of the interpretivist philosophy upon which we base this relationship. There is no point in using investigative ideas and introducing technical tools in a piecemeal fashion; the philosophy must drive the process and in this way the clients can remain the key players throughout and not the victims.

THE CASE STUDIES

Within the text we have presented an example of a 'real' study in which the clients participated in the development of a new information system and new methods of working. The success of the study seemed to have resulted from the clients' acceptance of ownership of the problem and the ISA's function in a secondary role, namely that of expert adviser with the clients very much in control. The library case study has been used successfully over several years and by students at different levels of study. The advantage of this case study lies in its flexibility—the fact that all students 'know' about libraries and the major input that IT can make (and will make) to this source of information (which is what a library is). The study, we believe, provides the student with an opportunity to think about the essence of the problem and its many facets, and demonstrates how the creative use of technology might enable all those involved to achieve what they want from the project. This includes the money-making desires of the property developer, the intellectual desires of the librarian and the political desires of the councillor. The study we believe is an ideal vehicle for the student to appreciate the benefits of client-led design.

INFORMATION SYSTEMS ANALYST

What is the real role of the ISA? The role of the ISA, following a successful implementation, will vary. If the ISA is a consultant, it is expected that periodically he or she will be required to attend a client meeting to give professional advice and from time to time help the clients to enhance their information system further. If the ISA is part of a large company, it is likely that the monitoring and control system for the company information system will continue to be an important part of his or her responsibilities.

The recognition of the need to develop company-wide information systems has been brought into focus by business requirements and not because of a desire to purchase computers for their own sake. The flexibility and the processing power of the technology provides the potential to reappraise the way in which an enterprise operates. However, the full exploitation of the technology can only be achieved by the clients and the ISA as expert adviser. The expertise of the ISA will almost certainly develop along the lines of a company expert in the provision enhancement and exploitation of information as a resource. The skill requirements of the modern ISA will need to match these demands. It is likely that the ISA, as in other professions, will specialize in particular domains such as business, medicine and law. It is fairly obvious that the ISA will need to possess as much knowledge of the domain as of the technology, but he or she will also need to possess a range of skills that will enable the best use of available technology to be attained. We have attempted in this text to describe some tools that may be useful in the identification and description of client information systems.

CONCLUSION

We hope that the ideas presented within this text will provide some useful practical tools that will aid the process of information definition and technical specification. It cannot be emphasized too strongly that client-led design is not a methodology but a framework through which a number of suitable design methods can be used. The framework itself is as much a statement of intent as anything else; and the most important attribute of the framework is its dedication to interpretivism.

We wish you good information systems practice.

REFERENCES

Ackoff, R.L. (1962) *Scientific Method: Optimising Applied Research Decisions*, New York: Wiley.

Ackoff, R.L. (1974) *Redesigning the Future: A Systems Approach to Societal Problems*, New York: Wiley.

Ackoff, R.L. and Emery, F.E. (1972) *On Purposeful Systems*, London: Tavistock Publications.

AIIE Committee Report (1951) 'Proposed symbols and terms for feedback control systems', *Electrical Engineering*, **70**, 909.

Albrow, M. (1973) 'The Study of Organisations—Objectivity or Bias' in *People and Organisations*' (ed. G. Salaman and K. Thompson), London: Longman, pp 396–413.

Ashby, W.R. (1958) *An Introduction to Cybernetics*, London: Chapman and Hall.

Ashby, W.R. (1978) *Design for a Brain* (2nd edn), London: Chapman and Hall.

Ashworth, W. (1986) 'The History of the British Coal Industry, vol. 1, no. 5, 1946–1982', *The Nationalised Industry*, Oxford: Clarendon Press.

Avison, D.E. and Fitzgerald, G. (1988) *Information Systems Development: Methodologies, Techniques and Tools*, Oxford: Blackwell.

Avison, D.E. and Wood-Harper, A.T. (1986), 'Multiview – An Exploration in Information Systems Development', *The Australian Computer Journal*, vol. 18, no. 4, November.

Avison, D.E. and Wood-Harper, A.T. (1990) *Multivew: an exploration in information systems development*, Oxford: Blackwell Scientific Publications.

Barnard, C. (1938) *The Functions of the Executive*, Cambridge, Mass.: Harvard University Press.

Beer, S. (1972) *Brain of the Firm*, Chichester: Wiley.

Bell, S. and Wood-Harper, A.T. (1992) *Rapid Information Systems Development*, Maidenhead: McGraw-Hill.

Benjamin, R.I. and Levinson, E. (1993) 'A framework for managing IT-enabled change', *Sloane Management Review*, vol. 34, no. 4, pp 23–34.

Benyon D. and Skidmore, S. (1987) 'Towards a toolkit for the systems analyst', *Computer Journal*, vol. 30, no. 1, pp 27.

Berger, P.L. and Luckmann, T. (1966) *The Social Construction of Reality*, New York: Doubleday.

Bertalanffy, L. von (1950) 'The theory of open systems in physics and biology', *Science*, **111**, 23–9.

Bertalanffy, L. von (1971) *General Systems Theory: Foundations Development Applications*, Harmondsworth: Penguin.

Bertalanffy, L. von (1981) 'General systems theory — a critical review', in *Systems Behaviour* (3rd edn) (ed.: The Open Systems Group), London: Harper and Row, pp 59–79.

Blackler, F. and Shimmin, S. (1984) *Applying Psychology in Organisations*, London: Methuen.

Blau, P.M. and Scott, W.R. (1962) *Formal Organisations*, San Francisco: Chandler.

Blau, P.M. and Scott, W.R. (1970) *Formal Organisations*, London: Routledge & Keegan Paul.

Blum, F.H. (1955) 'Action research — a scientific approach?', *Philosophy of Science*, **22** (1), 1–7.

Blumer, H. (1975) 'Sociological implications of the thought of George Mead', in: *Social Theory Revisited* (ed. C.J. Jesser), Hinsdale, Il·1.: Dryden Press.

Boland, R.J. (1985) 'Phenomenology: a preferred approach to research on information systems', in *Research Methods in Information Systems* (eds. E. Mumford, R.A. Hirschheim, G. Fitzgerald and A.T. Wood-Harper), Amsterdam: Elsevier, pp 193––201.

Booch, G. (1986) *Software Engineering with ADA*, Redwood City, California: Benjamin/Cummings.

Booch, G. (1991) *Object Oriented Design*, Redwood City, California: Benjamin/Cummings.

Buckingham, R.A., Hirschheim, R.A., Land F.F. and Tully, C.S. (1987), *Information Systems in Education: Recommendations and Implementation*, Cambridge University Press: Cambridge.

Burrell, G. and Morgan, G. (1979) *Sociological Paradigms and Organisational Analysis*, Aldershot: Gower.

Campbell, J. (1978) 'On the nature of organizational effectiveness', in *New perspectives on organizational effectiveness* (ed. P.S. Goodman), San Francisco: Jossey-Bass, pp 13–55.

Carter, R., Martin, J., Mayblin, B. and Munday, M. (1984) *Systems Management and Change*, London: Harper and Row.

Chambers (1990) *English Dictionary*, 7th edn, W. & R. Chambers Ltd, Edinburgh.

Checkland, P.B. (1976) 'Science and the systems paradigm', *International Journal of General Systems*, vol. 3, pp 127–134.

Checkland, P.B. (1979) 'The shape of the systems movement', *Journal of Applied Systems Analysis*, **6**, 129–35.

Checkland, P.B. (1981) *Systems Thinking, Systems Practice*, Chichester: Wiley.

Checkland, P.B. (1982) 'Soft Systems Methodology as process: a reply to M. C. Jackson', *Journal of Applied Systems Analysis*, **9**, 37–9.

Checkland, P.B. (1985) 'From optimizing to learning: a development of systems thinking for the 1990s', *Journal of the Operational Research Society*, vol. 36, no. 9, pp 757–767.

Checkland, P.B. (1986a) The politics of practice. Paper presented at International Roundtable on the Art and Science of Systems Practice, IIASA, No. 1986.

Checkland, P.B. (1986b) 'Systems thinking', *Systemist*, No. 20, 10–16.

Checkland, P.B. (1988) 'Images of systems and systems image', *Journal of Applied Systems Analysis*, vol. 15, pp 37–42.

Checkland, P.B. (1989a) 'Soft Systems Methodology', in: *Rational Analysis for a Problematic World* (ed. J. Rosenhead), Chichester: Wiley, pp 71–100.

Checkland, P.B. (1989b) 'O.R. and social science: fundamental thoughts', in: *Operational Research and the Social Sciences* (eds M.C. Jackson, P. Keys and S.A. Cropper), New York: Plenum Press, pp 35–41.

Checkland, P.B. (1989c) SSM—present and future. Keynote Address at the 2nd United Kingdom Systems Society Workshop, City University, 18-19 December 1989.

Checkland, P.B. (1989d) 'Researching systems methodology: some future prospects', in: *Systems Prospects: The Next Ten Years of Systems Research*, (eds R.L. Flood, M.C. Jackson and P. Keys), New York: Plenum Press, pp 9–15.

Checkland, P.B. and Casar, A. (1986) 'Vickers' concept of an appreciative system: a systemic account', *Journal of Applied Systems Analysis*, **13**, 3–17.

Checkland, P.B. and Davies, L.J. (1986) 'The use of the term Weltanschauung in soft systems methodology', *Journal of Applied Systems Analysis*, **13**, 109–15.

Checkland, P.B. and Scholes, J. (1990) *Soft Systems Methodology in Action*, Chichester: Wiley.

Churchman, C.W. (1968) *The Systems Approach*, New York: Delta Publishing.

Churchman, C.W. (1971) *The Design of Inquiring Systems: Basic Concepts of Systems and Organization*, New York: Basic books.

Clark, A.W. (1980) 'Action research: theory, practice and values', *Journal of Occupational Behaviour*, **1**, 151–7.

Clark, P.A. (1972) *Action Research and Organizational Change*, London: Harper and Row.

Coad, P. and Yourdon, E. (1990) *Object Oriented Analysis*, Englewood Cliffs, N.J., Prentice-Hall.

Collins (1992) *New compact English dictionary*, 2nd edn, Harper-Collins: Edinburgh.

Cooperrider, D.L. and Srivastva, S. (1987) 'Appreciative inquiry in organisational life', *Research in Organisational Change and Development*, **1**, 129–69.

Cox, B. (1987) 'Stress: coping and problem solving', *Work and Stress*, vol. 1, No. 1, Jan–March, pp 5–14.

Cyert, R.M. and March, J.G. (1963) *A Behavioural Theory of the Firm*, Englewood Cliffs, N.J.: Prentice-Hall.

Davies, L. and Ledington, P. (1991) *Information in action: soft systems methodology*, Macmillan Education Ltd: Basingstoke.

Davis, L.E. and Cherns, A.B. (1975) *Quality of Working Life*, New York: Free Press.

Dilthey, W. (1961) *Pattern and Meaning in History* (ed. H.P. Rickman), New York: Harper and Row.

Dilthey, W. (1969) *The Essence of Philosophy*, New York: AMS Press.

Dilthey, W. (1976) *Selected Writings* (ed. H.P. Rickman), Cambridge: Cambridge University Press.

Doyle and Wood (1991) 'Systems thinking, systems practice: dangerous liaisons', *Systemist*, vol. 13, no. 1, pp 28–30.

Emery, F.E. (ed.) (1969) *Systems Thinking*, vols 1, 2 and 3, Harmondsworth: Penguin.

Emery, F.E. and Trist, E.L. (1960) 'Socio-technical systems' in *Management sciences—models and techniques*, (eds C. West-Churchman and M. Verhulst), New York: Pergamon, vol. 2, pp 83–97.

Emery, F.E. and Trist, E.L. (1965) 'The causal texture of organisational environments', *Human Relations*, **18** (1), 21–32.

Erlichman, J. (1992a) 'Counter culture: fat profits that belie lean times in the High Street', *The Guardian*, 10th August, p 4.

Erlichman, J. (1992b) 'How hidden persuasion makes shoppers spend', *The Guardian*, 11th August, p 5.

Erlichman, J. (1992c) 'Counter culture: shoppers who find supply falls short of their demands', *The Guardian*, 12th August, p 5.

Espejo, R. and Harnden, R. (eds) (1989) *The Viable System Model: Interpretation and Application of Stafford Beer's VSM*, Chichester: Wiley.

Fayol, H. (1949) *General and Industrial Management*, London: Pitman.

Finkelstein, C. (1989) *An introduction to information engineering*, Addison-Wesley: Wokingham.

Flood, R.L. (1990) *Liberating systems theory*, New York: Plenum Press.

Flood, R.L. and Carson, E.R. (1988) *Dealing with Complexity: An Introduction to the Theory and Application of Systems Science*, New York: Plenum Press.

Forrester, J.W. (1961) *Principles of Systems*, Cambridge, Mass.: MIT Press.

Gadamer, H-G. (1975) *Truth and Method* (trans. and ed. G. Barden and J. Cumming), New York: Seabury Press.

Galliers, R. (ed.) (1987) *Information Analysis, Selected Readings*, Sydney: Addison-Wesley.

Gane, C. (1990) *Computer-aided Software Engineering*, Englewood Cliffs, N.J.: Prentice-Hall.

Gane, C. and Sarson, T. (1979) *Structured Systems Analysis*, Englewood Cliffs, N.J.: Prentice-Hall.

Garfinkel, H. (1968) *Studies in Ethnomethodology*, Englewood Ciffs, N.J.: Prentice-Hall.

Giddens, A. (1976) *New Rules of Sociological Method*, London: Hutchinson.

Gill, K.S. (1986) 'The knowledge-based machine: issues of knowledge transfer', in: *Artificial Intelligence for Society* (ed. K.S. Gill), Chichester: Wiley, pp 7–17.

Gilmore, T., Krantz, J. and Ramirez, R. (1986) 'Action based modes of inquiry and the host-researcher relationship', *Consultation*, **5** (3), 160–76.

Goldthorpe, J.H., Lockwood, D., Bechhofer, F. and Platt, J. (1968) *The Affluent Worker: Industrial Attitudes and Behaviour*, London: Cambridge University Press.

Gulick, L. and Urwick, L. (eds) (1937) *Papers in the Science of Administration*, New York: Institute of Public Administration, Columbia University.

Habermas, J. (1972) *Knowledge and Human Interests*, Boston: Beacon.

Handy, C. (1975) *Understanding Organisations*, Harmondsworth: Penguin.

Heron, J. (1977) *Catharsis in Human Development*, London: British Postgraduate Medical Foundation.

Herzberg, F., Mausner, B. and Snyderman, B. (1959) *The Motivation to Work*, New York: Wiley.

Hirschheim, R.A. (1985) 'Information systems epistemology: an historical perspective', in: *Research Methods in Information Systems*, (eds E. Mumford, R.A. Hirschheim, G. Fitzgerald and A.T. Wood-Harper), Amsterdam: Elsevier, pp 13–35.

Hirschheim, R.A. and Klein, H.K. (1989) 'Four paradigms of information systems developments', *Social Aspects of Computing*, **32** (No. 10; Oct.), 1199–1214.

Hirschheim, R.A. and Newman, A. (1988) 'Information systems and user resistance: theory and practice', *Computer Journal*, vol. 31, pp 398–408.

HMSO (1993) 'Applying soft systems methodology to an SSADM feasibility study', Information Systems Engineering Library (series), London.

Hult, M. and Lennung, S. (1980) 'Towards a definition of action research: a note and a bibliography', *Journal of Management Studies*, **17** (2), 241–50.

Jackson, M.C. (1982) 'The nature of 'soft' systems thinking: the work of Churchman, Ackoff and Checkland', *Journal of Applied Systems Analysis*, **9**, 17–29.

Jackson, M.C. (1983) 'The nature of 'soft' systems thinking: comment on the three replies', *Journal of Applied Systems Analysis*, **10**, 109–13.

Jackson, M.C. (1989) 'Future prospects in systems thinking', in: *Systems Prospects: The Next Ten Years of Systems Research* (eds R.L. Flood, M.C. Jackson and P. Keys) New York: Plenum Press, pp 73–80.

Jackson, M.C. (1991) *Systems methodology for the management sciences*, New York: Plenum Press.

Jackson, M.C. (1992) 'An integrated programme for critical thinking in information systems research', *Journal of Information Systems*, vol. 2, pp 83–95.

Jayaratna, N. (1988) 'Guide to methodology understanding in information systems practice,' *International Journal of Information Management*, vol. 8, 43–53.

Katz, D. and Kahn, R.L. (1966) *The social psychology and organisation*, New York: Wiley.

Klein, H.K. and Hirschheim, R. (1983) 'Issues and approaches in appraising technological change in the office: a consequentialist perspective', *Office, Technology and People*, vol. 2, no. 1, pp 15–42.

Klein, H.K. and Hirschheim, R.A. (1987) 'A comparative framework of data modelling paradigms and approaches', *Computer Journal*, **30** (1), 8–14.

Kling, R. (1987) 'Defining the boundaries of computing across complex organizations', in *Critical Issues in Information System Research* (eds R.J. Boland and R.A. Hirschheim), Chichester: Wiley, pp 307–362.

Klir, G.J. (1985) *Architecture of Systems Problem Solving*, New York: Plenum Press.

Koestler, A. (1967) *The ghost in the machine*, Hutchison: London.

Kuhn, T.S. (1962) *The Structure of Scientific Revolutions*, Chicago: The University of Chicago Press.

Land, F.F. (1985) 'Is an information theory enough?', *Computer Journal*, vol. 28, no. 3, pp 211–215.

Lewin, K. (1948) 'Action research and minority problems', in: *Resolving Social Conflicts*, (ed. G.W. Lewin), New York: Harper, pp 201–20.

Lincoln, Y.S. and Guba, E.G. (1984) *Naturalistic Inquiry*, California: Sage.

Lucas, H.C. (1974) 'Systems quality, user reactions, and the use of information systems', *Management Informatics*, vol. 3, no. 4, pp 207–212.

Lyytinen, K.J. and Klien, H.K. (1985) 'The critical theory of Jurgen Habermas as a basis for a theory of information systems', in: *Research Methods in Information Systems* (eds E. Mumford, R.A. Hirschheim, G. Fitzgerald and A.T. Wood-Harper), Amsterdam: North-Holland, pp 219–31.

Martindale, D. (1967) *The Nature and Types of Sociological Theory*, London: Routledge and Kegan Paul.

Maslow, A. (1943) 'A theory of human motivation', *Psychological Review*, **50**, 370–96.

Maturana, H.R. (1978) 'Biology of language: the epistemology of reality', in: *Psychology and Biology of Language and Thought: Essays in Honor of Eric Lenneberg* (eds G.A. Miller and E. Lenneberg), New York: Academic Press, pp 27–64.

Maturana, H.R. and Varela, F.J. (1987) *The Tree of Knowledge: The Biological Roots of Human Understanding*, Boston, Mass.: New Science Library.

Maude, T. and Willis, G. (1991) *Rapid prototyping: the management of software risk*, London: Pitman.

Mayo, E. (1949) *The Social Problems of an Industrial Civilization*, London: Routledge and Kegan Paul.

Mayr, O. (1969) *The Origins of Feedback Control*, Cambridge, Mass.: MIT Press.

McDermid, D.C. (1990) *Software Engineering for Information Systems*, Oxford: Blackwell.

Mead, G.H. (1934) *Mind, Self, and Society*, Chicago: University of Chicago Press.

Methlie, L.B. (1980) 'Systems requirements analysis—methods and models', in: *Information Systems Environment* (eds H.C. Lucas Jr, F.F. Land, T.J. Lincoln and K. Supper), Amsterdam: North-Holland, pp 173–85.

Miles, R.K. (1985) 'Computer systems analysis: the constraint of the hard systems paradigm', *Journal of Applied Systems Analysis*, vol. 12, pp 55–65.

Miles, R.K. (1988) 'Combining "soft" and "hard" systems practice: Graffinfor embedding', *Journal of Applied Systems Analysis*, vol. 15, pp 55–60.

Mingers, J. (1984) 'Subjectivism and soft systems methodology: A Critique', *Journal of Applied Systems Analysis*, **11**, 85–103.

Mintzberg, H. (1984) 'Power and organisational life cycles', *Academy of Management Review*, vol. 9, no. 2, pp 207–295.

Mooney, J.C. and Reiley, A.P. (1931) *Onward Industry*, New York: Harper and Row.

Morgan, G. (1986) *Images of Organisation*, London: Sage.

Mumford, E. and Henshall, D. (1979) *A participative approach to computer system design*, London: Associated Business Press.

Mumford, E. and MacDonald, W.B. (1989) *XSEL's Progress: The Continuing Journey of an Expert System*, Chichester: Wiley.

Mumford, E. and Weir, M. (1979) *Computer Systems in Work Design—The ETHICS Method*, London: Associated Business Press.

Naughton, J. (1979) 'Functionalism and systems research: a comment', *Journal of Applied Systems Analysis*, **6**, 69–73.

Nelson, C. (1986) 'The design of well-adapted and adaptable computer-based information systems', *Journal of Applied Systems Analysis*, vol. 13, pp 33–51.

Oppelland, H.J. and Kolf, F. (1980) 'Participative development of information systems: methodological aspects and empirical experiences', in: *The Information Systems Environment*, (eds H.C. Lucas, Jr., F.F. Land, T.J. Lincoln and K. Supper), Amsterdam: North-Holland, IFIP, pp 218–238.

Oquist, P. (1978) 'The epistemology of action research', *Acta Sociologica*, **21** (2), 143–63.

Palmer, R.E. (1969) *Hermeneutics*, Evanston: Northwestern University Press.

Parker, L.D. (1984) 'Control in organisation life: the contribution of Mary Parker-Follett', *Academy of Management Review*, **9** (Nov.) 736–45.

Parkin, A. (1987) *Systems Analysis* (2nd edn), London: Arnold.

Pask, G. (1976) *Conversation Theory: Applications in Education and Epistemology*, Amsterdam: Elsevier.

Pask, G., Scott, B.C.E. and Kallikourdis, D. (1973) 'A theory of conversations and individuals', *International Journal of Man–Machine Studies*, **5**, 443–566.

Penguin (1985) *The Penguin dictionary of computers*, Harmondsworth: Penguin.

Peters, M. and Robinson, V. (1984) 'The origins and status of action research', *Journal of Applied Behavioural Science*, **20** (2), 113–24.

Pfeffer, J. (1981) *Power in organisations*, Massachusetts: Pitman.

Pidd, M. (1984) *Computer Simulation in Management Science*, Chichester: Wiley.

Plutchik, R. (1974) *Foundations of Experimental Research* (2nd edn), New York: Harper and Row.

Popper, K.R. (1959) *The Logic of Scientific Discovery*, London: Hutchinson.

Popper, K.R. (1983) *Objective Knowledge: An Evolutionary Approach*, (rev. edn), Oxford: Oxford University Press.

Popper, K.R. and Eccles, J.C. (1977) *The Self and Its Brain*, New York: Springer International.

Prevost, P. (1976) ' 'Soft' systems methodology, functionalism and the social sciences', *Journal of Applied Systems Analysis*, **5** (1), 65–73.

Prior, R. (1991) 'Dangerous liaisons: a reply to Doyle and Wood', *Systemist*, vol 13, no. 2, May, pp 81–90.

Prior, R. (1992) 'Linking SSM and IS development', *Systemist*, vol. 13, no. 2, May, pp 81–90.

Pugh, D.S., Hickson, D.J. and Hinings, C.R. (1980) *Writers on Organisations* (2nd edn), Harmondsworth: Penguin.

Pugh, D.S., Hickson, D.J. and Hinings, C.R. (1985) *Writers on organisations*, Harmondsworth: Penguin.

Punch, M. (1986) *The Politics and Ethics of Fieldwork*, Beverly Hills, CA: Sage.

Rapoport, R.N. (1970) 'Three dilemmas in action research', *Human Relations*, **23** (6), 499–513.

Reason, P. and Rowan, J. (eds) (1981) *Human Inquiry: A Sourcebook of New Paradigm Research*, Chichester: Wiley.

Rickman, H.P. (1976) *Dilthey: Selected Writings*, London: Cambridge University Press.

Roberts, N., Anderson, D., Deal, R., Garet, M. and Shaffer, W. (1983) *Introduction to Computer Simulation: A System Dynamics Modeling Approach*, Reading, MA: Addison-Wesley.

Robey, D. and Farow, D. (1982) 'User involvement in information system development: a conflict model and empirical test', *Management Science*, vol. 28, no. 1, pp 73–85.

Rudman, B. (1992) 'The secret of successful feasibility studies in SSADM', *SSADM Newsletter*, no. 13, March p 10.

Rzevski, G. (1988) 'IT strategy and quality of information systems teaching: improving the practice (ISTIP '88)' *Proceedings of the Information Systems Association Conference*, Civil Service, Sunningdale, pp 123–128.

Sawyer, K. (1992) 'A contribution towards the debate on linking SSM to IS', *Systemist*, vol. 14, no. 3 pp 199–201.

Schoderbek, C.G., Schoderbek, P.P. and Kefalas, A.G. (1990) *Management Systems: Conceptual Considerations* (4th edn), Dallas: Business Publications.

Schutz, A. (1971) *Collected Papers I: The Problem of Social Reality*, The Hague: Martinus Nijhoff.

Schwartz, H. and Jacobs, J. (1979) *Qualitative Sociology: A Method to the Madness*, New York: Free Press.

Schwartz, P. and Ogilvy, J. (1979) 'The emergent paradigm: changing patterns of thought and belief', *Analytical Report 7, Values and Lifestyles Program*, Menlo Park, CA: SRI International.

Silverman, D. (1981) *The Theory of Organisations: A Sociological Framework*, London: Heinemann.

Silverman, D. (1985) *Qualitative Methodology and Sociology: Desribing the Social World*, Aldershot: Gower.

Simon, H.A. (1957) *Administrative Behaviour: A Study of Decison Making Processes in Administrative Organisation* (2nd edn), New York: Collier/Macmillan.

Smyth, D.S. and Checkland, P.B. (1976) 'Using a systems approach: the strucutre of root definitions', *Journal of Applied Systems Analysis*, **5** (1), 75–83.

SSADM (1990) SSADM Version 4 Reference Manuals, July, NCC. Oxford: Blackwell.

Stansfield, M.H. (1990) *The Development of an Expert System to Aid the User of Soft Systems. Methodology*, MSC Project, School of Informational Science, Portsmouth Polytechnic (unpublished).

Steers, R.M. (1975) 'Problems in the measurement of organisational effectiveness', *Administrative Science Quarterly*, vol. 20, no. 4, pp 546–558.

Stevens, R. (1990) 'Humanistic psychology', in: *Introduction to Psychology*, Vol. 1 (ed. I. Roth), Hove: Larence Erlbaum Associates in association with the Open University, pp 418–69.

Stowell, F.A. (1984) Waverly-Randall Project Documents (unpublished).

Stowell, F.A. (1985) 'Experiences with SSM and data analysis', *Information Technology Training*, 48–50.

Stowell, F.A. (1989) *Change, Organisational Power and the Metaphor 'Commodity'*, Unpublished PhD thesis. Department of Systems, University of Lancaster.

Stowell, F.A. (1990) 'Implications of advances in information technology and the changing role of the systems analyst', *Systems Analysis, Modelling, Simulation*, vol. 7, pp 17–24.

Stowell, F.A. (1991) 'Towards client-led development of information systems', *Journal of Information Systems*, **1**, 173–89.

Stowell, F.A. (1994) 'Empowering the client—the relevance of SSM and inter-pretivism to client-led design', in: *Information Systems Definition: The Contribution of Soft Systems Methodology* (ed. F.A. Stowell), Maidenhead: McGraw-Hill (in press).

Stowell, F.A. and West, D. (1990) 'The contribution of systems ideas during the process of knowledge elicitation', in: *Systems Prospects: The Next Ten Years of Systems Research* (eds R.L. Flood, M.C. Jackson and P. Keys), New York: Plenum Press, pp 329–34.

Stowell, F.A. and West, D. (1992) 'SSM as a vehicle for client-led design of information systems: utilising "Ideal-type" Mode 2', *Systemist*, vol. 14, no. 3, pp 99–106.

Stowell, F.A. and West, D. (1994) 'Client-led design of information systems: an application of "ideal-type" mode 2 soft systems methodology', *Journal of Information Systems*, vol. 4, no. 2, pp 117–127.

Straub, D.W. and Trower, J.K. (1988) 'The importance of user involvement in successful systems: a meta-analytical reappraisal', Working Paper MISRC-WP-89-01, Management Informations Systems Research Centre, University of Minnesota, Minneapolis, MN.

Susman, G.I. and Evered, R.D. (1978) 'An assessment of the scientific merits of action research', *Administrative Science Quarterly*, **23**, 582–602.

Tate, B. and Jones, L. (1975) *Systems, Models and Decisions*, T341 1/2 The Open University, Technology: A Third Level Course Systems Modelling Units 1/2.

Taylor, F.W. (1947) *Scientific Management*, London and New York: Harper Row.

Trist, E.L. and Bamforth, K.W. (1951) 'Some social and psychological consequences of the Longwall method of coal getting', *Human Relations*, **4**, 38.

Tsoukas, H. (1991) 'The missing link: a transformational view of metaphors in organisational science', *Academy of Management Review*, **16** (3), 566–85.

Tsoukas, H. (1993) 'Analogical reasoning and knowledge generation in organisations theory', *Organisation Studies*, vol. 14, pp 323–404.

Van Gigch, J.P. (1988) 'Diagnosis and metamodelling of systems failures', *Systems Practice*, vo. 1, no. 1, pp 31–45.

Varela, F.G., Maturana, H.R. and Uribe, R. (1974) 'Autopoiesis: the organization of living systems, its characterization and a model,' *BioSystems*, 5, 187–96.

Vickers, G. (1965) *The Art of Judgement: A Study of Policy Making*, London: Chapman and Hall.

Vickers, G. (1968) *Value systems and social process*, New York: Basic Books.

Vickers, G. (1970) *Freedom in a Rocking Boat*, London: Allen Lane.

Vickers, G. (1973) *Making institutions work*, London: Associated Business Programmes.

Vickers, G. (1978) Presidential Address: 22nd North American Annual Meeting of the International Society for General Systems Research, Washington D.C.

Vickers, G. (1983) *Human Systems Are Different*, London: Harper and Row.

Vickers, G. (1984) *The Vickers papers*, London: Harper and Row.

Vickers, G. (1987) *Policymaking, Communication and Social Learning* (eds G.B. Adams, J. Forester, and B.L. Catron), New Jersey: Transaction.

Ward, P.T. (1989) How to integrate object orientation with structure analysius and design, *IEEE Software*, vol. 6, no. 2, pp 74–82.

Waring, A. (1989) *Systems Methods for Managers: A Practical Guide*, Oxford: Blackwell.

Warmington, A. (1980) 'Action research: its methods and its implications, *Journal of Applied Systems Analysis*, **7**, 23–39.

Weber, M. (1949) *The Methodology of the Social Sciences*, Glencoe, Ill.: Free Press.

Weber, M. (1964) *The Theory of Social and Economic Organisation*, New York: Free Press.

West, D. (1990a) 'Appreciation', 'expertise' and knowledge elicitation—the relevance of Vickers' ideas to the design of expert systems', *Journal of Applied Systems Analysis*, **17**, 71–8.

West, D. (1990b) 'Knowledge elicitation as an inquiring system: towards a knowledge elicitation methodology', in: *Proc. 34th Meeting of the International Society for Systems Science*, 8–13 July 1990, Oregon, USA, pp 1165–71.

West, D., Stansfield, M.H., and Stowell, F.A. (1994) 'Using computer-based techno-logy to support a subjective method of inquiry', *Systems Practice*, vol. 7, no. 2.

Willcocks, L. and Lester, S. (1993) 'How do organizations evaluate and control information systems investments? Recent UK survey evidence', in: *Human, organizational, and social dimensions of information systems development*, (eds D. Avison, J.E. Kendall, and J.I. De Gross), Amsterdam: North-Holland, pp 15–39.

Wilson, B. (1984) *Systems: Concepts, Methodologies and Applications*, Chichester: Wiley.

Wilson, B., (1990) *Systems concepts, theory, methodologies and applications* (2nd edn) Chichester: Wiley.

Winograd, T. and Flores, F. (1986) *Understanding Computers and Cognition: A New Foundation for Design*, Norwood, N.J.: Ablex.

Wood, J.R.G. (1992) 'Linking soft systems methodology and information systems', *Systemist*, vol. 14, no. 3, pp 133–135.

Wood-Harper, A.T. and Fitzgerald, G. (1982) 'A taxonomy of current approaches to systems analysis', *The Computer Journal*, no. 25, pp 12–16.

Wood-Harper, A.T., Antill, L. and Avison, D.E. (1985) *Information systems definition: the multiview approach*, London: Blackwell.

Young, A. (1987) *The Arthur Young practical guide to information engineering*, New York: Wiley.

AUTHOR INDEX

Ackoff, R. L., 17, 41, 55
Albrow, M., 26
Anderson, D., 74
Ashby, W. R., 77
Ashworth, W., 27
Avison, D. E., 29

Barnard, C., 105, 106
Bechhofer, F., 92, 106
Beer, S., 108
Benjamin, R. I., 140
Benyon, D., 5
Berger, P. L., 121, 126, 129
Blackler, F., 26, 100
Blau, P. M., 97
Blum, F. H., 122
Blumer, H., 125
Booch, G., 29, 86, 88
Buckingham, R. A., 7
Burrell, G., 96, 102, 106, 107, 108, 109,
    111–112, 129

Campbell, J., 102
Carson, E. R., 26
Casar, A., 115, 116
Checkland, P. B., 16, 17, 18, 33, 41, 47, 51,
    91, 110, 111, 115, 118, 122, 124,
    125, 126, 131, 133, 135, 160, 168
Cherns, A. B., 107
Churchman, C. W., 10, 17, 41, 118
Clark, A. W., 132, 133
Clark, P. A., 127
Coad, P., 88
Cooperrider, D. L., 125
Cox, B., 100
Cyert, R. M., 100, 106

Davies, L., 30
Davis, L. E., 107
Deal, R., 74
Dilthey, W., 50, 118, 128
Doyle, K., 30

Emery, F. E., 26, 27, 121, 135
Erlichman, J., 102
Espejo, R., 108
Evered, R. D., 123, 124, 125, 126, 127–128,
    130, 131, 133

Fayol, H., 94
Flood, R. L., 26, 41
Flores, F., 6, 9, 40, 122, 126
Follett, 29, 113
Forrester, J. W., 74

Galliers, R., 98
Gane, C., 85
Garet, M., 74
Garfinkel, H., 125, 126
Giddens, A., 126
Gill, K. S., 125
Gilmore, T., 129, 131
Goldthorpe, J. H., 92, 106
Guba, E. G., 122, 125, 126, 135
Gulick, L., 94

Habermas, J., 124, 126
Handy, C., 26
Harnden, R., 108
Henshall, D., 29
Herzberg, F., 107
Hickson, D. J., 26, 107
Hinings, C. R., 26, 107
Hirschheim, R. A., 7
Hult, M., 127

Jackson, M. C., 17, 41, 122
Jacobs, J., 124, 125
Jayaratna, N., 5

Kahn, R. L., 26
Katz, D., 26
Kefalas, A. G., 16, 21, 96
Klien, H. K., 5, 9, 16
Koestler, A., 16
Krantz, J., 129, 131
Kuhn, T. S., 126

Land, F. F., 7
Ledington, P., 30
Lennung, S., 127
Levinson, E., 140
Lewin, K., 107, 121, 125, 127, 135
Lincoln, Y. S., 122, 125, 126, 135
Lockwood, D., 92, 106
Luckmann, T., 121, 126, 129
Lyytinen, K. J., 5, 9, 16

MacDonald, W.B., 124
March, J. G., 100, 106
Maturana, H. R., 121, 122
Maslow, A., 107
Maude, T., 29
Mausner, B., 107
Mayr, O., 123
McDermid, D. C., 85
Mead, G. H., 129
Methlie, L. B., 5, 6
Miles, R. K., 9, 30
Mintzberg, H., 26
Mooney, J. C., 94
Morgan, G., 96, 102, 103, 104, 106, 107,
    108, 109, 110, 111–112, 129
Mumford, E., 29, 107, 124

Nelson, C., 5

Oquist, P., 122, 128, 129, 130, 133

Parker, L. D., 29, 113
Peters, M., 127, 133, 135
Pfeffer, J., 26
Pidd, M., 74
Platt, J., 92, 106
Plutchik, R., 124
Popper, K. R., 124, 126
Prior, R., 30
Pugh, D. S., 26, 107
Punch, M., 124

Ramirez, R., 129, 131
Rapoport, R. N., 127, 133
Reason, P., 122, 125
Reiley, A. P., 94
Rickman, H. P., 50
Roberts, N., 74
Robinson, V., 127, 133, 135
Rowan, J., 122, 125
Rudman, B., 85
Rzevski, G., 28

Sarson, T., 85
Sawyer, K., 30

Schoderbek, C. G., 16, 21, 96
Schoderbek, P. P., 16, 21, 96
Scholes, J., 16, 17, 122, 135
Schutz, A., 125, 126, 135
Schwartz, H., 124, 125
Scott, W. R., 97
Shaffer, W., 74
Shimmin, S., 26, 100
Silverman, D., 104, 126, 129, 133
Simon, H. A., 106
Skidmore, S., 5
Snyderman, B., 107
Srivastva, S., 125
Stansfield, M. H., 78
Steers, R. M., 102
Stevens, R., 125
Stowell, F. A., 27, 28, 30, 38, 100, 101, 160,
    188
Susman, G. I., 123, 124, 125, 126, 127–128,
    130, 131, 133

Taylor, F. W., 94, 96
Trist, E. L., 26, 27, 121, 135
Tsoukas, H., 101
Tully, C. S., 7

Urwick, L., 94

van Gigch, J. P., 21
Vickers, G., 15, 33, 41, 49, 54, 56, 110,
    114–119, 123

Ward, P. T., 86
Warmington, A., 122
Weber, M., 121, 125, 133
West, D., 173
Weir, M., 107
Willis, G., 29
Wilson, B., 29, 55, 56, 127, 135
Winograd, T., 6, 9, 40, 122, 126
Wood, J. R. G., 30
Wood-Harper, 29

Yourdon, E., 88

SUBJECT INDEX

Action research, 32, 107, 121–135
Activity models, 80–81, 169
Appreciation, 25, 33–34, 37, 54, 93, 110,
    114-18, 123, 130, 132
Appreciative system, 114–116, 129
Awareness, 25, 58–59

Black box diagrams, 62, 74–76, 167
Boundary, 44–47
Business organizations, 92–94

Causal loop diagrams, 71–74
Change, 7, 27–31, 101, 107
Classical management theory, 93, 94–96,
    102–103
Client-led design, 22, 31, 55, 83, 140–199
    framework, 31–37
    object orientation, 85–88
    phase I, 33–35, 51, 91, 140–169
    phase II, 35, 172–179
    phase III, 35–36, 179–196
    phase IV, 36, 196–197
    phase V and VI, 37, 197–198
Closed system, 94, 96, 104
Communication, 47
Complexity, 40
Computer system, 4
Computer systems analyst, 4, 5, 10
Conceptual model, 80
Connectivity, 42–43
Contectivity, 42–43
Context, 25–26, 43, 92
Control, 48–49
Control models, 48, 62, 65–71, 98–99
Critical systems thinking, 41
Cybernetics, 108

Data, 11–15
Datalogical, 5
Decision table, 67
Decision tree, 67
Design methods, 8

Emergence, 51–52
Emergent property, 27, 51
Environment, 44–47
ETHICS, 107

Equilibrium models of organization, 93,
    103–108

Feedback, 67–71
    positive, 69, 71
    negative, 69–71
Functionalist paradigm, 102, 108, 111–112
    systems thinking, 109–112

Goals, 117
goal-seeking, 34, 96–98
models of organization, 93, 94–96, 98–103

Hard systems thinking, 41
Hard versus soft systems thinking, 19–21,
    41–42, 109–114
Hawthorne studies, 106–107
Hermeneutic cycle, 128
Hierarchy, 47
History, 123
Holism, 42–43
Holistic, 18
Human activity systems, 109, 110, 118
Human nature, 113–114
Human relations theory, 107
Hypotheses 124–5, 126

Implementation, 36
Individual perspective, 49–51
Influence diagram, 71
Infological, 5
Information, 11–15, 48
Information system, 4, 6, 7
definition, 21
Information systems analyst, 4, 5, 6, 25
as faciliator, 38–40
Inquiring system, 114–118
Inquiry, 114, 122–123, 135
Interaction, 109
Interpretive paradigm, 109, 111–112
Interpretive systems thinking, 108, 109–119
Intervention, 104, 109

Knowledge, 113, 126, 128, 131–133

Learning, 93, 108–110, 111, 114, 119, 130

Measurement, 125
Meta-discipline, 18
Methodology, 114
Methods, neutrality of, 123–4
Models, 35, 55–5
    of organization, 91–119
Multiview, 29

Notional system, 42, 57–58, 60

Object-oriented analysis, 9, 81, 85
Object-oriented design, 29, 86
Observer/observed, 122–3, 130
Open loop control, 65–66
Open systems, 93, 101, 103–5, 108
Optimizing, 104 108, 111, 119
Organizational culture 25–28, 37, 51, 92, 100
Organizational models, 93–119
Organizations, 91–120

Positivist, 10
Positivist empiricism, 121–126
Power, 29
Problem appreciation, 110
    analysis, 30
Prototyping, 29
Purposeful systems, 131

Quality of working life, 107–108

Rationalistic, 10
Reality, 102, 113, 122, 126, 128, 129
Reductionism, versus holism, 17–19, 42–44
Reductionist, 18
Relationship-maintaining models of
    organization, 93, 108–119
Relationship-maintenance, 116–117
Repeatability, 124–125
Requisite variety, 77
Rich pictures, 62, 77–80
Rigour, of action research, 133

Satisficing, 93
Scientific management theory, 95–96,
    102–103
Scientific method, 121–126
Socio-technical systems, 107
Soft Systems Methodology (SSM), 77,
    111–112
Soft Systems thinking and client-led design,
    40
Spray diagrams, 62–63, 164
Structured data flow diagrams, 62
Structured diagrams, 84
Structured methods, 81
Structured systems analysis and design method
    (SSADM), 10
Sub-system, 44–47
Synergy, 51–52
System, 4, 15–16, 44–47
Systems concepts, 42–52
    diagrams and models, 60–84
    dynamics, 74
    maps, 43–44, 62, 64–65
    theory and practice, 19
    thinking and information systems, 16
    client-led design, 40–53
    tools, 61

Tavistock Institute, 107, 127
Technical specification, 35–36
Technology-based information system, 4
Transformation, 57, 58, 176

Viable systems model, 108

Waverly-Randall Case Study, 139–198
Weltanschauung, 50, 118
Wholeness, 41, 42